ACROSS THE OCEAN SEA
A Journal of Columbus's Voyage

ACROSS THE OCEAN SEA

A Journal of Columbus's Voyage

by GEORGE SANDERLIN
Illustrated by Laszlo Kubinyi

HARPER & ROW, PUBLISHERS ~ NEW YORK

*Grateful acknowledgment is made for permission
to reprint selections from the following books:*

THE DIALOGUES OF PLATO. Translated by B. Jowett. By permission of the Clarendon Press, Oxford.

THE LIFE OF THE ADMIRAL CHRISTOPHER COLUMBUS BY HIS SON FERDINAND. Translated by Benjamin Keen. Copyright © 1959 by Rutgers, The State University. Published by Rutgers University Press.

THE BOOK OF SER MARCO POLO. Reprinted with permission of The Macmillan Company from THE BOOK OF SER MARCO POLO, edited by George B. Parks. Copyright 1927 The Macmillan Company.

THE NORTHMEN, COLUMBUS AND CABOT. Edited by J. E. Olson and E. G. Bourne. Copyright renewed by Barnes & Noble, Inc., 1934. All rights reserved. Reprinted 1959.

THE JOURNAL OF CHRISTOPHER COLUMBUS. Translated by Cecil Jane. Copyright © 1960 by Clarkson N. Potter, Inc. Used by permission of Clarkson N. Potter, Inc., and Eugenio Cassin editore.

VOYAGES TO VINLAND. Reprinted with permission of Alfred A. Knopf, Inc., from VOYAGES TO VINLAND by Einar Haugen. Copyright 1941, 1942 by Einar Haugen and Frederick T. Chapman.

Selections from the following books are reprinted by permission of The Hakluyt Society, London, and Cambridge University Press, New York, as publishers on behalf of the Society:
MANDEVILLE'S TRAVELS. Edited by Malcolm Letts.
SELECT DOCUMENTS ILLUSTRATING THE FOUR VOYAGES OF COLUMBUS. Edited by Cecil Jane.
THE LETTERS OF AMERIGO VESPUCCI. Edited by Clements R. Markham.

ACROSS THE OCEAN SEA: A JOURNAL OF COLUMBUS'S VOYAGE
Text copyright © 1966 by George Sanderlin
Illustrations copyright © 1966 by Laszlo Kubinyi

Library of Congress Catalog Card Number: AC 66-10296

To Johnny

Contents

Maps and Illustrations

Author's Note

Most of this book consists of selections from Columbus's *Journal* for his voyage of 1492–93 and from original sources for earlier voyages and legends of the Atlantic. Omission of some of the words of the original source within a sentence is indicated by three dots; omission of a sentence or more from the source is indicated by four dots. In a few places, sentences of the original source are transposed so that the order of events will be clearer.

Place names and names of persons are standardized (e.g., "Kinsay" for "Quisay," "Columbus" for "Colon"). Names of persons and places connected with Columbus are usually given in the forms adopted by Samuel Eliot Morison in his *Journals and Other Documents on the Life and Voyages of Christopher Columbus.* Names of other persons and places are given in the forms adopted by Boies Penrose in his *Travel and Discovery in the Renaissance.*

Words inserted by a translator to make his meaning clear and enclosed by him in brackets are not bracketed here. Words inserted by the present editor for additional information (e.g., "*Niña*" after "the caravel") are bracketed. Words inserted by the present editor in place of a word or phrase of the original source are bracketed. Punctuation and capitalization of the sources are, for the most part, retained, but the paragraphing is the present editor's.　　　　　　　　　　　　　　　　　　G.S.

Introduction

What would the world be like without the Statue of Liberty and the Declaration of Independence? Without the idea of a frontier to be conquered, the memory of pioneers crossing the prairies in covered wagons? What would the world be like without Forty-Niners, gauchos, wigwams and Indian peace pipes, the dark green stillness of the Amazon or the Christ of the Andes? What would the world be like without the Americas?

It is hard for us to imagine. Europeans of the late Middle Ages looked out on the Atlantic Ocean to their west with thoughts very different from ours. Not only were they unaware of the existence of our two continents; they also did not know some common facts about the oceans. For example, they did not know that nearly three-fourths of the earth is covered with water; or that if you dropped Mt. Everest into the deepest part of the Pacific Ocean, its peak would be six thousand feet below passing ships; or that if you evaporated all the water in the oceans you would be left with a pile of salt bigger than Africa.

On the other hand, we speak of the "oceans," when it might be better to say, with men of the fifteenth century, "the Ocean" or "the Ocean Sea." We think of the three great oceans—the S-shaped Atlantic, and the circular Pacific and Indian oceans—as lying between continents, like huge lakes. But they all run together at the bottom of the world, and there is more water (the Arctic Ocean) at the top. It would be more accurate to call the continents "islands" which are surrounded by ocean. As a matter of fact, our word "ocean" is related, through the Greek οκεανος, to a Sanskrit word that meant "surrounding."

As men visualized it before the Age of Discovery, the world, which was generally agreed to be round, consisted of just one great land mass or *orbis terrarum* ("circle of lands") surrounded by the Ocean Sea. The *orbis terrarum* included the three connected continents of Europe, Asia, and Africa. It was sometimes called the Island of Earth.

Before 1400, Europeans had sailed over only 7 per cent of the waters of the world. They crept along familiar coasts in their small boats, and often landed to sleep or even to eat. They could find their way around an inland sea like the Mediterranean, and across the narrow northwestern part of the Indian Ocean, but they did not dare sail far into the Atlantic.

In the west the Strait of Gibraltar was for many years the end of the known world. It took great daring to venture out to the Canary Islands and the Madeiras, which lie near the coast of Morocco. Beyond these islands the Ocean Sea was a realm of mystery.

Common seamen tugged on their red stocking caps and strained their eyes for the sight of land as they exchanged legends about the Atlantic. Flying dragons and griffins—creatures half eagle, half lion—were said to lurk in its fogs. The Bishop of the Seas, with his phosphorescent miter, might rise from its depths, or the Sea Unicorn, whose horn could transfix three ships at once! If you sailed too far out, you might fall off; and if you were white and sailed into the Torrid Zone, the sun would roast you, and you would turn black. The sea boiled there, and the water ended in a hideous swamp filled with serpents.

For the men of western Europe as for the Moslem Arabs who had overrun North Africa and Spain, the Atlantic was the "Green Sea of Darkness."

"The Western Ocean is boundless," said an Arab geographer of the fourteenth century. "Ships dare not venture out of sight of land, for . . . they would run the risk of being lost in mist, fog, or vapor."

Yes, agreed another Arab writer; no one dares embark on the Green Sea of Darkness because giant whirlpools would swallow his ship. And scholars who explained the Koran, the Mohammedan Bible, recommended that a man insane enough to sail west in the Ocean Sea be deprived of his civil rights.

Was there any other land out in the Ocean Sea? Several Greek writers thought that a land mass was needed in the Southern Hemisphere to balance the *orbis terrarum* in the North Temperate Zone; otherwise, the globe would be topheavy, like a ball with a blob of mud on its upper surface. The Greeks called such a hypothetical southern land the *Antipodes*, meaning "feet against." But theologians of medieval Europe persuaded most geographers not to accept the Greek theory. How could Christ's Gospel, said to have been preached to the ends of the earth, have been carried across the Ocean Sea, they asked.

Anyhow, if there ever were any men and women of the Antipodes, with "feet against" ours, such upside-down people would long ago have fallen headfirst into space.

So much for the Antipodes. But what about the Western Hemisphere? Suppose you sailed from Europe over the western horizon?

If you survived, if you escaped the flying dragons, you might look for fabled islands, mountains, even a continent imagined by earlier writers. After Hercules struck the rocks at the western end of the Mediterranean with his club and allowed its waters to rush out into the vast Ocean, Greek and Roman poets and philosophers speculated about the Green Sea of Darkness.

In the fourth century B.C. the Greek philosopher Plato "invented America." That is, he made up a story about a huge island named Atlantis, larger than Asia Minor and North Africa combined, located somewhere in the Atlantic west of Gibraltar. Atlantis was a powerful and splendid kingdom, whose temples gleamed with marble and red-gold "orichalcum." And beyond Atlantis was a "boundless continent."

Plato's story of Atlantis, which he said was destroyed by an earthquake nine thousand years before his time, and of the "boundless continent" beyond, fascinated later readers. After America was discovered, one Elizabethan geographer, John Dee, wanted to call the new lands Atlantis, and another, Richard Hakluyt, thought that Plato had "plainly described the West Indies." Some observers thought that the Sargasso Sea, the two-thousand-mile patch of gulfweed which floats in mid-Atlantic, marked the location of the sunken Atlantis.

In Roman times the biographer Plutarch made some guesses about the smaller islands Plato had placed near Atlantis. Plutarch named one of these islands Ogygia, and said that from Ogygia you could row a mere five hundred miles to a "great continent." One scholar has identified Ogygia with Greenland.

Seneca, a playwright and philosopher living under the Emperor Nero, prophesied that some day "new worlds" would be discovered beyond Iceland. He said that "from the farthest shores of Spain westward to those of India" was only "a very few days' sail."

Readers of the books of Plato, Plutarch, and Seneca were not seamen. The Green Sea of Darkness remained frightening, and unexplored. In the Middle Ages, however, writers added to the library of mythical stories about its waters.

One of the most popular stories was of the voyage of St. Brendan. St. Brendan was an Irish monk. He had his hair tonsured, in the Irish fashion, in the form of a cross—that is, shaved from ear to ear and from forehead to neck. He sailed in a coracle, a round boat made of hides stretched over a wooden framework, not much larger than a washtub. In the sixth century he was supposed to have made a marvelous seven-year cruise from Galway, past Hostile and Friendly Whales, to islands of Sheep, of Smiths, and of Small Dark Fiends, and at last to the wide Land Promised to the Saints. Some Irishmen today wish to identify his Land Promised to the Saints with America.

Mapmakers of the later Middle Ages faithfully placed "St. Brendan's Islands" on their charts, at first west of Ireland, later west of Spain—farther and farther west as they failed to appear to voyagers. Expeditions were still looking for them as late as 1721!

Dante, greatest of medieval poets, located his mountain of Purgatory in the midst of the Ocean Sea, directly opposite Jerusalem. Purgatory was not depicted on maps and charts, but Antillia, also called "Island of the Seven Cities," was. Antillia was supposed to have been discovered and colonized by seven refugee Portuguese bishops and their congregations who were escaping from the Arabs in the eighth century. Mapmakers placed Antillia west of Spain; on one chart it was only 2,500 miles from Japan—a convenient way station for ships bound west for the Orient.

Medieval mapmakers often depicted disk-shaped Brazil (an imaginary island named after an Irish demigod, not the South American country, which is named after a red dyewood) and crescent-shaped Mayda. Both were shown off Ireland. There was an Island of Demons farther west (near Labrador), named for the diabolical weather sent down from the arctic, and a Cradle Island farther east —a floating maternity ward where women of another imaginary isle went to bear their children.

In fact, the famous Greek geographer Ptolemy, followed by the Arab Edrisi, sprinkled the Atlantic with 27,000 islands! When serious attempts began to be made to conquer the Ocean Sea, in the fifteenth century, "island hunting"—with a promise from your king that you could be viceroy of any islands you found—was a favorite sport of ambitious captains and shipowners.

Myths and legends fed men's imaginations and made them stare out at the stormy Atlantic, from Galway to Cadiz, with mingled fear and fascination. The search for imaginary islands led to the discovery of several real ones. The dream of Atlantis to some extent dispelled the frightful apparitions of flying dragons, giant cuttlefish which might seize a ship in their arms, or the Sea Unicorn.

But the Green Sea of Darkness still concealed in "mist, fog, or vapor" its profound secret. No one truly suspected the existence—outside the *orbis terrarum* of Europe, Asia, and Africa—of another great land mass. Most still agreed with the medieval traveler, John Marignolli, who declared: "God did not wish the human race to sail around the world."

Until 1492, except for the Vikings, men of the so-called Western civilization remained imprisoned on their Island of Earth, not yet daring to test their dreams by voyaging farther west.

Of course, it was not easy to sail into the unknown. Sailing west on the Ocean Sea was like leaving a familiar countryside of farms and villages and plunging into a dark forest without a guide. Suppose you couldn't find your way back?

From early times, however, seamen *did* venture for short distances into the Western Ocean. Even though their ships were not much larger than a modern liner's lifeboats, Phoenicians, Greeks, and Romans sailed through the Pillars of Hercules (the Strait of Gibraltar) and returned with news about the coasts to the north and south.

The Phoenicians of Palestine were a hardy, close-mouthed race of merchants and seafarers. Their basket-shaped vessels were seen along the Atlantic front of Spain as early as 1100 B.C., when the Phoenicians founded Cadiz. They also established colonies on the Atlantic coast of Morocco. According to one doubtful report of the Greek historian Herodotus, they made a three-year voyage from the Red Sea all the way around Africa and back by way of Gibraltar (600 B.C.).

The Greeks and Romans were not as much at home on the sea as the Phoenicians. Their ships were not well adapted to ocean voyaging—neither their war galley, a swift, narrow vessel with a ram at the prow, walking over the water on its flashing banks of oars like a centipede, nor their tubby merchant ship with one mast and one large square sail. Nevertheless, both Greeks and Romans found their way to the Canary Islands, which they knew as the "Fortunate Islands" (*Insulae Fortunatae*)—although the

Canaries are now named for the large dogs (Latin *canis*) which the Romans saw there. The Romans also knew the Madeiras as the "Purple Islands" (*Purpuriae*). Of course the legend that Ulysses founded Lisbon is unhistorical.

Around 320 B.C. the Greek explorer Pytheas sailed from Marseilles, in southern France, north to Britain and Scotland. In Scotland he heard of a land named Thule, probably Iceland. *Ultima Thule*—"farthest Thule"—became a name for the most remote outpost of the *orbis terrarum*, like our "outer space."

"Atlantic" is derived from "Atlas," a towering Moroccan mountain range overlooking the ocean. The Norsemen were the first to conquer a part of this ocean. Their famous longships and merchant *knorrs*, undecked vessels 60 to 70 feet long propelled by oars and one large, striped square sail, rode over the Atlantic rollers. Steered by an oar lashed to the right side at the stern (the "steerboard" side, whence our word "starboard"), with a carved gilt sea serpent's head at the prow, these ships carried the Vikings to Iceland, Greenland, and, finally, North America.

(When the Norse reached Iceland, in the ninth century, they found that Irish hermits had been there. These monks, true sons of St. Brendan, had made a remarkable early voyage from Ireland.)

Bjarni Herjulfson, an alert Viking trader, and the gallant adventurer Leif Ericson, were the heroes of the conquest of the northern route to America, A.D. 986–1000. Bjarni reconnoitered New England; Leif Ericson afterward landed there, or farther south, where the grape grows wild. But northern clouds soon closed around the Vikings' discoveries. They could not maintain their foothold against the attacks of the Indians. The rest of Europe

paid no attention to a few reports of a distant western island named Vinland. The Green Sea of Darkness remained a realm of mystery.

During the Dark Ages (A.D. 500–1100), even the
Canary Islands and the Madeiras slipped back behind the
curtain of Atlantic fog. Cape Nun, just around the corner
from Gibraltar in Morocco, was the end of the line for
Moslem and Christian ships alike. In the twelfth century
eight Moors of Lisbon, the "Lisbon Wanderers," are said
to have sailed as far as the Sargasso Sea, in mid-Atlantic,
then touched at the Canaries on their return voyage—but
their exploit may have been imagined.

Then, slowly, after the year 1200, ships, seamen, and
their primitive instruments of navigation all began to improve. The steering oar was replaced by a rudder, hung
on the stern post. The triangular lateen sail, which enabled a ship to tack, that is, to sail at an angle against the
wind, was borrowed from the Arabs. Men now had the
compass to sail by, the magnetized needle whose pointing
north was for a while considered magical.

The needle was attached to the underside of a circular
card marked with the thirty-two compass points (a fleur-
de-lis at the north, a cross at the east, etc.); the card was
mounted in a circular bowl so as to turn freely, like a
roulette wheel. The compass may have been invented in
Genoa; its origin is obscure, but Genoese were in the van-
guard of the new attack upon the Green Sea of Darkness.

Around 1270 a Genoese fleet under Lancelot Malocello
sailed boldly into the Atlantic and rediscovered the
Canary Islands. No sooner were mapmakers affixing the
red cross of Genoa to these isles than two brothers of that
city, the Vivaldi, in 1291, equipped two galleys and departed for India by sea, attempting a feat that would not

be accomplished until Vasco da Gama's voyage two hundred years later. They sailed down the African coast past Cape Nun, were reported off Guinea, then disappeared in the lonely south Atlantic. In 1317 a Genoan became the first admiral of the new Portuguese navy. Probably Italians were the rediscoverers of the Madeiras; these islands are shown on maps after 1338.

Voyages continued to be made along the African coast, such as that of the Spaniard Jaime Ferrer in 1346, seeking a "River of Gold" (*Rio del Oro*), and the early attempts of the Portuguese to get past the cape below Cape Nun —Cape Bojador ("Cape Bulge"), a low point with a dangerous reef swept by fierce currents. But seamen did not sail far out of sight of the sandy African shore.

For the permanent conquest of the Ocean Sea, men needed a leader. In the fifteenth century Prince Henry the Navigator took command. He established a base on Cape St. Vincent, a bleak promontory at the southwestern tip of Europe which became the Cape Kennedy of that day. Here his shipwrights designed the graceful caravel, a long, light ship, relatively low in the water, carrying three lateen sails—a ship destined to take the Portuguese to the ends of the earth. From here he sent his mariners to find out "the nature of the land beyond that Cape [Bojador]" and also to seek "knowledge . . . of the Indies."

Broad-shouldered, black-haired Prince Henry was chiefly interested in pushing back the curtain of darkness to the south—reaching the gold, ivory, and slaves of the rich Guinea Coast, and finding a sea route to India. But he also sent ships west into the Atlantic to colonize the Madeiras and to attempt to conquer the Canaries, rediscover the Azores, and investigate the mythical Island of the Seven Cities.

In 1431 Gonçalo Velho made a daring voyage more than eight hundred miles west of Lisbon, trusting to his seamanship and his compass to bring him back from the Green Sea of Darkness. Prince Henry had told him to look for the "Fortunate Isles, or Isles of St. Brendan"—and Velho found the Azores. In 1456 the Venetian Cadamosto, also sailing for Prince Henry, was blown west during an African voyage and discovered the arid Cape Verdes, three hundred miles out at sea.

But the Azores, ten rainy green isles thick with hawks and buzzards (Portuguese *açor* means "hawk") were what brought the Portuguese within striking distance of the unknown western goal. The Azores are only 1,054 miles from Newfoundland. Intermittently, from 1452 to 1487, bold, profit-seeking Portuguese captains voyaged beyond the Azores, looking for land.

All were defeated by the Green Sea of Darkness; all returned empty-handed, buffeted by wind and high seas. They failed because in the latitude of the Azores the strong westerlies blow the year round, making the Atlantic there a one-way street for sailing vessels. The Portuguese were going the wrong way.

Yet the seamen of the maritime peoples of southern Europe—Portuguese, Spanish, Genoese, Venetian, French —now had the equipment needed for a successful western voyage. In addition to the graceful caravel (50–200 tons), they had the roomier if clumsier *nao* (often over 400 tons) with three square sails, seaworthy in the "black tempests" of the Atlantic. They had improved astrolabes and quadrants, for observing the sun or North Star, with which to determine latitude—their distance, in degrees, north or south of the equator. (The height of the North Star in degrees above the horizon *is* the latitude of the ob-

server.) They had world maps with geographers' edu-
cated guesses about the location of Cathay (China) and
Cipangu (Japan), and they could draw upon a wealth of
sailing experience.

What was now required was a man of imagination,
daring, and genius. And "Genoa the Proud," the great
seaport of northwestern Italy which may have invented
the compass and which had pioneered in ocean voyaging
during the Middle Ages, provided him.

His name was Christopher Columbus.

"It was a gentle custom of the ancients to number
amongst the gods those heroes by whose genius and greatness of soul unknown lands were discovered," wrote Peter
Martyr, the sixteenth century historian.

Christopher Columbus—Cristoforo Colombo—was not a
demigod, nor even of the nobility like da Gama and
Magellan, but the son of a wool weaver. He was born in
September or October, 1451, in Genoa, that "noble and
powerful city by the sea," as he himself described his
birthplace. And in spite of his service under foreign rulers,
he was to remain a citizen of Genoa all his life, proud of
its seafaring traditions and far-ranging traders.

Here he passed his boyhood. A tall, hawk-nosed, red-
haired dreamer, he stared out at carracks and galleys anchored in the blue half circle of the harbor, or in ship
chandlers' establishments peered at astrolabes, maps, and
compasses. In the upper town, where Genoa climbs the
hills of the Ligurian Alps in a tangle of narrow streets,
lanes, and stairways, he wandered past splendid residences
and medieval churches with striped façades of black and
white marble. But he had to go home to a small house, with
its looms and cramped living quarters for the Colombos—

his father Domenico, his mother Susanna, and his younger brothers and sister, Bartholomew, Giovanni, Giacomo, and Bianchinetta.

Christopher was imaginative, but he was also conscientious and hardworking. Along with his brother Bartholomew, he became a skillful wool carder, and spent long hours wielding the two flat boards covered with teeth that separated and mixed the fibers. By the time he was twenty-two he was co-signing contracts to purchase wool with his father, also an agreement to sell a house.

He was too ambitious to be shiftless like the good-hearted Domenico, who, when he once operated a tavern, was "the sort of wineseller who was his own best customer." But years later Christopher expressed his affection for his father by naming Hispaniola's capital city, now the oldest European town in the Americas, after Domenico's patron saint: Santo Domingo.

How could an alert youth with Christopher's hopes and dreams escape from his father's weave room? Education was a road closed to the children of the lower middle class. Christopher was still almost illiterate; he spoke the dialect of Genoa, but could not write the very different Tuscan, the literary language of Italy. Later, like many immigrants, he acquired the language of the country he resided in, Spanish with Portuguese spellings. He picked up some Latin, read widely, and became self-educated. But this was after he had left wool weaving—for the sea.

War and trade in the Mediterranean gave him his chance, and he took it. In 1474 or 1475 he was one of the workmen enlisted in a Genoese expedition to defend Chios against the Turks. On this voyage past historic Greece and Crete to the craggy isle in the eastern Mediterranean, Christopher learned to handle a tiller and reef a sail. But the Turks did not appear, so the force returned to Genoa.

In 1476 he embarked as a common seaman on a merchant convoy sailing for Lisbon, England, and Flanders to market a resin called mastic, produced on Chios. Suddenly, off Cape St. Vincent, Portugal, Christopher found himself fighting for his life—wrestling stone balls into the breech of a cannon and firing into a curtain of smoke and flame as a French-Portuguese fleet attacked the Genoese. (France was at war with Burgundy, and Columbus's ship, the *Bechalla*, was sailing under the Burgundian flag.)

This was the heroic action Christopher had dreamed of! He was wounded, but he fought on until his ship began to sink and he leaped into the sea.

Then his exhilaration must have given way before the cold shock of being face-to-face with death. The coast of Portugal was six miles distant. Fortunately he saw a sweep floating amid some wreckage. He seized it, pushed it before him, and alternately swimming and resting, at last reached the shore.

The Portuguese treated him kindly (Genoa and Portugal were not at war) and nursed him back to health. But Columbus was probably changed by his narrow escape— less romantic in his dreams, more fiercely determined to use the time God had given him for some great achievement.

What great achievement?

In 1477, if not before, its outline must have been emerging. Arriving penniless in Lisbon, Columbus signed on a Portuguese ship engaged in the prosperous trade with the Azores, Bristol, and Iceland. When his ship reached Galway, Ireland, he saw two castaways who made him ponder deeply.

"A man and a woman of remarkable appearance adrift

in two boats," Columbus later described them. They were flat-faced, probably Finns or Laplanders, but Columbus's considered explanation was: "Men of Cathay, in the East, have come here."

If men of China could voyage east to Europe, why could not men of Europe sail west to China?

On the last leg of the voyage Columbus wrote: "In the month of February, 1477, I sailed one hundred leagues beyond the island of Thule [Iceland]. . . . To this island, which is as big as England, the English come with their wares, especially from Bristol. When I was there, the sea was not frozen."

Even this far north the Ocean Sea was open; there was not even any drift ice, which the Greek Pytheas called "jellyfish," perhaps because of its movement. It is unlikely that Columbus heard of the Norse voyages to Vinland, but if he did the stories would only have increased the confidence he was beginning to feel that the Ocean Sea was navigable far to the west.

He returned to Lisbon to set up a chartmaking business with his brother Bartholomew, who had arrived earlier. Both Colombos had probably learned chartmaking in Genoa; Genoese charts were used by every seafaring nation. An acquaintance describes Christopher at this time as "a seller of printed books . . . a man of keen intelligence though with small book learning, expert in the art of cosmography and the making of world maps." Christopher had his eyes open to new developments: printing was then only about twenty-three years old.

From 1477 to 1485 Columbus studied Spanish, Latin, and geography, listened to the talk of Portuguese seamen, and made more voyages with them. He sailed as a commercial agent to Madeira and as a ship's officer to Elmina, on the African Gold Coast, where he saw people living in the Torrid Zone, which some geographers still said was uninhabitable. He mastered navigation, the care of a ship, and trading with primitive peoples. On the African voyage he established his own measurement for a degree of longitude, something he would have to know if he planned to sail west.

"It was in Portugal," wrote Columbus's son Ferdinand, "that the Admiral [Columbus] began to think that if men could sail so far south, one might also sail west and find lands in that quarter."

In Portugal also, Columbus married and by the age of thirty, when his red hair turned gray, had his feet planted on the ladder to success. Nothing is known of Dona Felipa Perestrello e Moniz, whom Christopher met at the chapel of the Lisbon convent school she attended, except that she was of a good but impoverished family. Her noble father, Bartholomew Perestrello, had been one of the colonizers of the island of Porto Santo, next to Madeira; not a very good colonizer, however, because he brought to the island a female rabbit which started a family that grew so rapidly the rabbits destroyed the farmers' crops. Christopher and Dona Felipa were married in 1479 and lived for a while on Porto Santo, where their only child, Diego, was born in 1480.

At this time, Columbus served as a trusted agent for Genoese merchants who wished to purchase sugar on Madeira. His charts continued to be in demand, and his wife's high-ranking relatives might someday prove helpful to him. It was his imagination and genius that, in the next few years, were to bring him to the verge of ruin—imagination and genius expressed in one fervently held idea.

He had become sure, "as certain . . . as if he held it in

a chest under lock and key," said Bishop Las Casas, who knew Columbus, that he could find his way to the riches of the East by sailing where men had never dared to sail before: west across the "boundless" Ocean Sea.

"Aristotle [says that] between the end of Spain and the beginning of India is a small sea, navigable in a few days."

Christopher Columbus finished writing this comment in the margin of Pierre d'Ailly's *Imago Mundi*, a fourteenth century geography, then rubbed his tired eyes and straightened the big folio to read further. It was the year 1485, and he was alone in Lisbon with five-year-old Diego. Felipa had died some time before.

Now he raised his pen again, not hearing the cry of the midnight watch outside, to underline part of a sentence by the "modern" d'Ailly: "The end of the habitable earth in the East and the end of the habitable earth in the West are near, and between is a *small sea*."

King John II's committee of experts would have to believe him in the morning! For the hundredth time Columbus reviewed the evidence he had collected to persuade the Portuguese king to sponsor his westward voyage, to give him three ships, the title of Admiral, and the position of viceroy over any islands or mainlands he discovered on his way to the Indies. . . .

There were the "man and . . . woman of remarkable appearance adrift in two boats" off Galway, and, later, washed up on the island of Flores in the Azores, two dead bodies exactly like those broad-faced Galway castaways.

There was Diogo de Teive, who in 1452 had suspected he was near land to the west when sailing in the latitude of Ireland. There was also that mysterious one-eyed sailor who had buttonholed Columbus at the harbor of Santa

Maria, in the Azores, and told about a voyage west of
Ireland on which the seamen saw "land [which] . . .
they imagined . . . was Tartary [northeast Asia]."

If these hints did not convince the experts, what about
the driftwood carved with some instrument other than an
iron one, not like wood worked in Europe, which Columbus's brother-in-law had picked up on the beach of Porto
Santo? Or the canes so thick that a joint would hold two
quarts of wine, also found on Porto Santo? Bamboo did
not grow in Europe—it was a calling card from Asia!

As for authorities, in addition to Aristotle and Pierre
d'Ailly, there was Marinus of Tyre, the teacher of the
famous Greek geographer Ptolemy (Columbus liked
Marinus's making Asia even wider than Ptolemy had);
the Florentine geographer Paolo Toscanelli (another
"wide Asia" man) who had written Columbus an encour-
aging letter; the Arab geographer Alfragan, who had
the right idea about the size of a degree of longitude (a
small size, to shrink the Ocean Sea for Columbus's voyage); Seneca with his statements and his prophecy; and . . .
and . . . Columbus shook himself awake. He would find
others!

But the next day brought rejection. The committee did
not like his minuscule degree of longitude (Columbus had
reduced this east-west measurement 25 per cent from the
true figure). They said he underestimated the circumference of the globe (they were right). They concluded that
his idea was "simply founded on imagination, or things
like that Isle Cipangu of Marco Polo." (Conservative
geographers were still skeptical about the existence of
Japan, first described by Marco Polo.)

"A big talker and boastful . . . full of fancy and imagination with his Isle Cipangu," agreed King John II, ac-

cording to the Portuguese historian Barros. Something about Columbus's voluble arguing made King John remember the Genoan—but he was dismissed.

Columbus had dreamed while Lisbon slept on its hills. Promoting his project had consumed time and money, bills for Felipa's funeral remained unpaid, little Diego's needs increased—now he awoke to find himself bankrupt.

Any "sensible" man would have cast Aristotle and Pierre d'Ailly into Lisbon Harbor and worked to recoup his losses. Instead, Christopher left the chartmaking business to Bartholomew and, furtively to avoid creditors, shipped himself, five-year-old Diego, and his troublemaking "Enterprise of the Indies" in a vessel bound for Spain, to try his luck there.

He and Diego landed at small, sleepy Palos, a few miles up the Rio Tinto, where southern Spain faces the Atlantic. Compared to Lisbon, Palos on its marshland was a dreary place, with no forest of tall masts in its harbor, no crowds of seamen of all nations in its streets. But the men of this Niebla district *were* experienced in making voyages to Africa in the slave trade—and anyhow, Columbus was undaunted.

His first step was to march Diego back down the river shore to a promontory on which gleamed the whitewashed walls and red tile roof of the Franciscan monastery of La Rabida. He had decided that Diego needed better care than he could give his son while demonstrating to shortsighted monarchs and mathematicians the advantages of the westward voyage.

"I'm thirsty." Diego clutched his father's big hand.

"The friars will give us water," said Christopher kindly as he knocked on the monastery door.

Diego got his drink, and also a home for six years with

the brown-robed brothers. But Columbus's knock opened doors in Seville as well as La Rabida.

Fray Juan Pérez, head of La Rabida, was interested in Columbus's "Enterprise" and sent him on to Fray Antonio de Marchena, head of the Franciscan subprovince of Seville and a good astronomer. Fray Antonio de Marchena recommended that Columbus apply to a certain wealthy nobleman, who almost gave him backing; then a second nobleman, the Count of Medina Celi, agreed to provide Columbus "with three or four well-equipped caravels, for he asked no more."

The count decided, however, that Ferdinand and Isabella should be consulted on so important a matter, and so sent Columbus south to Cordova, where, in May, 1486, he had his first audience with Queen Isabella.

In the gracious, auburn-haired Isabella of Castile, Columbus saw a ruler who might not be able to read sea charts, but who would sympathize with his desire to be a "Christ Bearer" (the meaning of "Christopher"), that is, the man to carry Christianity overseas. She and her husband, Ferdinand of Aragon, were in the midst of a crusade to drive the Moslems out of the Spanish peninsula. The defect accompanying Isabella's conventional piety, the bigotry which would soon lead her to sign the decree expelling the Jews from Spain, did not injure Columbus.

She listened to him attentively, but referred his project to a learned committee under her confessor Talavera. After hearing Columbus's arguments at the University of Salamanca, this committee conferred—for four years. At times Columbus was reduced to depending on friends like the Count of Medina Celi for food and shelter. But worse was the mockery of the courtiers ("When do you plan to voyage to the moon, Master Christopher?"), which made his cheeks burn and his blue eyes flash dangerously, even while he bit his tongue.

In his suffering Columbus turned to Beatriz Enríquez de Harana, a peasant girl whose family lived near Cordova. There was no marriage because marriage to a peasant would have handicapped Columbus at court. But in 1488 Beatriz became the mother of his son Ferdinand.

In this same year Columbus was invited to Portugal by King John II to discuss the westward voyage once more. Unfortunately he arrived just as Bartholomew Dias sailed into Lisbon Harbor, back from his epic discovery of the Cape of Good Hope and the eastern sea route to India. John II's last flicker of interest in Columbus was now extinguished. While his brother Bartholomew traveled to England and France to try to win the rulers of those countries over to the "Enterprise of the Indies," Christopher returned to Spain.

There, in 1490, Isabella's leisurely experts concluded their deliberations. Columbus had failed again. His voyage, said the committee, would take three years; there was no land on the other side of the globe anyhow, because St. Augustine said there was none; everything worth discovering had already been found; and in sailing westward over the horizon the ships would be going *downhill*, but in returning they would have to sail *uphill*.

"And that is something which ships cannot do!" declared several indignant committeemen.

The Talavera committee was a good one, but not really as knowledgeable as the Portuguese mathematicians. Queen Isabella, still trusting her instinct, pigeonholed their report. After the dramatic surrender of Granada, the Moslems' last stronghold, January 2, 1492, she gave Columbus a final chance before two more groups. But his "Enterprise" failed for the third time.

Then, reluctantly, Isabella stood beside wily Ferdinand and, in a formal audience at Granada, dismissed Christopher Columbus from Spain.

Columbus should now, at last, have given up. Very likely he did swear his favorite mild oath, "By San Fernando!" But then, without further hesitation, he packed his saddlebags and prepared to journey to the French court to see if he could do better there than Bartholomew so far had done.

This passionate and imaginative Genoan, having lost his wife, was now married to an idea—apparently, for worse. Isabella had wished to decide two questions: (1) Was his scheme, in the opinion of navigators and geographers, practicable? (2) Could the Crown, hard-pressed by war expenses and the shortage of gold and silver, afford the cost?

She could not override two vetoes. But when Luís de Santangel, Keeper of the Privy Purse, told her that he "marveled to see . . . her Highness . . . lack [resolution]" for such a glorious undertaking, and that he would finance the voyage himself if necessary, Isabella threw the experts' recommendations to the winds. She did not understand navigation, but she recognized character. Columbus's dedication and faith were now enough for her, and she sent a messenger after him and Fray Juan Pérez, who rode with him, to summon the Genoan.

To Granada? wondered Fray Juan Pérez as Isabella's marshal galloped up.

To Granada—and then Cipangu! thought Columbus, his heart leaping at the hint of Isabella's change of mind.

But both were wrong.   To America.

The two thousand years' quest for land to the west of
the known *orbis terrarum* (Europe, Asia, Africa) culmi-
nated in Columbus's voyage. And this had an aftermath of
bewilderment, and painful groping toward a revolutionary
new idea: that outside the *orbis terrarum* a "fourth part,"
a "new world," did in fact exist.

America, glimpsed and lost by Norsemen, permanently
rediscovered by Columbus, and finally recognized by the
merchant voyager Vespucci and the mapmaker Waldseemüller, then takes its place in the Western universe.

From the point of view of the Spanish Crown, the expedition commanded by Columbus represented a desperate
"long shot" gamble for victory in the race to the East, a
race which the Portuguese were about to win. Once Isabella had made her decision, financing the fleet did not
prove difficult. Isabella did offer to raise the money by
pawning her jewels, but this proved unnecessary. Santangel, the kingdom of Aragon, and Columbus himself
helped; cheap trading goods and provisions for a year were
supplied, and the ships were ready to sail within six
months.

From the point of view of Columbus, the voyage af-
forded an opportunity to vindicate his judgment, to gain
riches, to be a "Christ Bearer" and carry the Christian
faith to Asia.

But from our point of view, Columbus's achievement
was greater than even he imagined, the destination he arrived at more golden than the Cathay he thought he had
found. For us the ghosts of Forty-Niners and gauchos, of
Simón Bolívar and Thomas Jefferson, of bands playing

"The Battle Hymn of the Republic," of Presidents and astronauts, of Mother Cabrini, Gabriela Mistral, and Mark Twain—all crowd the poop of the *Santa María* and stare over his shoulder into the Green Sea whose darkness at last begins to lift.

On August 3, 1492, half an hour before dawn, three small ships raised their anchors, dropped down the Rio Tinto, crossed the bar of Saltés, and left man's ancient Island of Earth behind. Soon they were only specks in a wilderness of water. But ahead lay unsuspected new freedoms, new hopes for the future.

Ahead lay the Americas.

Chapter One

~⚬

LEGENDS OF
THE ATLANTIC

*There will come a time in the later years when
Ocean shall loosen the bonds by which we have been
confined, when an immense land shall be revealed and
[another] Tiphys [the pilot of the Argonauts] shall
disclose new worlds, and Thule [Iceland] will no
longer be the most remote of countries.*

—SENECA, *Medea*

The story of Atlantis is a dream about the past which turned out to be a prophecy of the future. The dreamer was Plato, the famous Greek philosopher of the fourth century B.C.

Plato, an aristocrat and champion wrestler in his youth, was a disciple of the burly, ugly Socrates, who was teaching Athens—and Europe—how to think by asking questions. "What is a state?" Socrates asked the youths who thronged around him. "What is just? What is unjust? What is the beautiful?" He asked such searching and uncomfortable questions that the reactionary party of Athens condemned him to death.

After Socrates had been forced to drink the poison hemlock, Plato devoted himself to spreading Socrates' ideas. Plato wrote his works in dialogue form, in imitation of Socrates' question-and-answer method, and introduced Socrates as his chief character. Plato also founded the first school of philosophy in a grove named Academus (whence our word "academy") outside Athens.

One of Plato's writings, *The Republic*, asks the question "What is justice" and tries to answer it by showing what justice is in the state—in an ideally just state or "Utopia." In Plato's next work, *The Timaeus*, Socrates wishes that he could "hear someone tell of our own city [the ideal republic] carrying on a struggle against her neighbors, and how she . . . showed . . . greatness."

In reply, another character tells a story he says came from Egypt. This story describes Athens of nine thousand years before Plato's time as equal to the ideal Republic in its customs, and tells how this ancient Athens defeated the forces of a great island kingdom, named Atlantis, in the Atlantic Ocean when Atlantis invaded the Mediterranean.

The selection below is the speech of the Egyptian priest about the war between Athens and Atlantis.

Many great and wonderful deeds are recorded of your state in our histories. But one of them exceeds all the rest in greatness and valor. For these histories tell of a mighty power which unprovoked made an expedition against the whole of Europe and Asia, and to which your city put an end.

The power came forth out of the Atlantic Ocean, for in those days the Atlantic was navigable; and there was an island situated in front of the straits which are by you called the Pillars of Heracles. The island was larger than Libya [North Africa] and Asia [Minor] put together, and was the way to other islands, and from these you might pass to the whole of the opposite continent which surrounded the true ocean. For this sea [the Mediterranean], which is within the Straits of Heracles, is only a harbor, having a narrow entrance, but that other is a real sea, and the surrounding land may be most truly called a boundless continent.

Now in this island of Atlantis there was a great and wonderful empire which had rule over the whole island and several others, and over parts of the continent, and, furthermore, the men of Atlantis had subjected the parts of Libya within the columns of Heracles as far as Egypt, and of Europe as far as Tyrrhenia [Italy]. This vast power . . . endeavored to subdue at a blow our country and yours and the whole of the region within the straits.

And then . . . your country shone forth, in the

excellence of her virtue and strength, among all mankind. She . . . was the leader of the Hellenes. . . . Having undergone the very extremity of danger, she defeated and triumphed over the invaders, and preserved from slavery those who were not yet subjugated, and generously liberated all the rest of us who dwell within the pillars.

But afterward there occurred violent earthquakes and floods; and in a single day and night of misfortune all your warlike men in a body sank into the earth, and the island of Atlantis in like manner disappeared in the depths of the sea. For which reason the sea in those parts is impassable . . . because there is a shoal of mud in the way; and this was caused by the subsidence of the island.

Atlantis is a "bad" Utopia which falls before the "good" Utopia, ancient Athens. Atlantis would remind Athenians of Persia, the powerful eastern empire which had attempted to conquer Greece just before Plato's time. Atlantis was a western Persia, a "great Barbarian" from the Ocean Sea.

Plato may have heard reports of fighting between tribes living outside Gibraltar and those of the Mediterranean shore. Or rumors of the floating mass of gulfweed in the mid-Atlantic, the Sargasso Sea, may have made him suppose there was a large sunken island there. Ancient navigators also imagined there was a muddy, shallow area in the Atlantic near Gibraltar.

In the following selection from the *Critias*, an unfinished dialogue about Atlantis and its war with Athens, Plato describes Atlantis in more detail.

Poseidon, receiving for his lot the island of Atlantis, begat children by a mortal woman, and settled them in a part of the island, which I will describe. Looking toward the sea, but in the center of the whole island, there was a plain which is said to have been the fairest of all plains and very fertile. Near the plain again, and also in the center of the island . . . there was a mountain not very high on any side. . . .

He . . . [brought] up two springs of water from beneath the earth, one of warm water and the other of cold, and [made] every variety of food to spring up abundantly from the soil. He also begat and brought up five pairs of twin male children; and dividing the island of Atlantis into ten portions, he gave to the first-born of the eldest pair . . . the largest and best, and made him king over the rest. . . .

And he named them all; the eldest . . . he named Atlas, and after him the whole island and the ocean were called Atlantic. . . . Now Atlas had a numerous and honorable family, and they retained the kingdom . . . for many generations. And they had such an amount of wealth as was never before possessed by kings. . . . For because of the greatness of their empire many things were brought to them from foreign countries, and the island itself provided most of what was required. . . .

In the first place, they dug out of the earth . . . orichalcum [copper alloy] . . . [which was] more precious in those days than anything except gold.

There was an abundance of wood for carpenter's work, and sufficient maintenance for tame and wild animals. Moreover, there were a great number of elephants in the island. . . . Also whatever fragrant things there now are in the earth, whether roots, or herbage, or woods, or essences which distill from fruit and flower, grew and thrived in that land; also the fruit which admits of cultivation. . . .

Meanwhile, they went on constructing their temples and palaces and harbors and docks. . . . The entire circuit of the wall, which went round the outermost zone, they covered with a coating of brass, and the circuit of the next wall they coated with tin, and the third, which encompassed the citadel, flashed with the red light of orichalcum. . . .

Poseidon's own temple . . . [had] a strange barbaric appearance. All the outside . . . with the exception of the pinnacles, they covered with silver, and the pinnacles with gold. In the interior of the temple the roof was of ivory . . . and . . . the walls and pillars and floor they coated with orichalcum. In the temple they placed statues of gold: there was the god himself standing in a chariot—the charioteer of six winged horses . . . around him . . . a hundred Nereids [sea nymphs] riding on dolphins. . . .

They had fountains, one of cold and another of hot water. . . . They constructed buildings about them and planted suitable trees; also they made cisterns, some open to the heavens, others roofed over,

to be used in winter as warm baths; there were the kings' baths, and the baths of private persons, which were kept apart; and there were separate baths for women. . . .

Of the water which ran off they carried some to the grove of Poseidon, where were growing all manner of trees of wonderful height and beauty . . . while the remainder was conveyed by aqueducts along the bridges to the outer circles. . . . There were many temples . . . also gardens and places of exercise, some for men, and others for horses . . . and . . . there was . . . a racecourse of a stadium in width, and in length allowed to extend all around the island, for horses to race in. . . .

The docks were full of triremes and naval stores, and all things were quite ready for use.

When Plato finished writing these passages about Atlantis, he had given Europe another question to think about, one which was to fascinate it for two thousand years:

Were there islands or mainlands beyond the Pillars of Hercules, in the boundless Ocean Sea? *Could* you reach land by sailing west?

ST. BRENDAN'S VOYAGE

Just as the first monks and hermits of Egypt sought solitude in the desert, so their later northern followers settled in forests, on mountains, and on offshore islands. In obedience to dream-visions, Irish monks even made mysterious voyages on the Ocean Sea.

The most famous of these voyages was a legendary one by St. Brendan, the "Christian Ulysses." The historical St. Brendan lived from 484 to 578, and was the founder of a monastery at Clonfert, Ireland, where he had three thousand disciples. He is thought to have sailed to the islands off the coast of Scotland, and to Wales, but no farther. The St. Brendan of the fictitious tenth century *Navigatio*, on the other hand, is the hero of a seven-year voyage through an Ocean Sea full of islands and marvels to the Land Promised to the Saints—which some Irish scholars would like to identify with America.

St. Brendan's voyage became one of the most popular of medieval sagas. According to one version, the Land Promised to the Saints was revealed to him in a vision in which he "saw the mighty intolerable ocean on every side and . . . the beautiful noble island, with trains of angels rising from it." According to another, a "holy abbot" named Barinthus first told him of it.

In one version Brendan searched first for the island in his small coracle—a boat made of greased skins stretched over a wooden frame—then returned to Ireland and, on the advice of a "holy woman," constructed a larger wooden boat in which he sailed with sixty followers. According to other versions the voyage was nonstop; at least there was no return to Ireland until the end, and the number of monks was smaller.

An ancient map tradition connects St. Brendan with the Canary Islands or with the Madeiras. As early as 1275 the Canary Islands are labeled on one map "Six Fortunate Islands are Islands of St. Brendan." In the fourteenth and fifteenth centuries, several maps call the Madeiras "The Islands of St. Brendan." Porto Santo ("Holy Port"), one of the Madeiras, is said to have been so named because St.

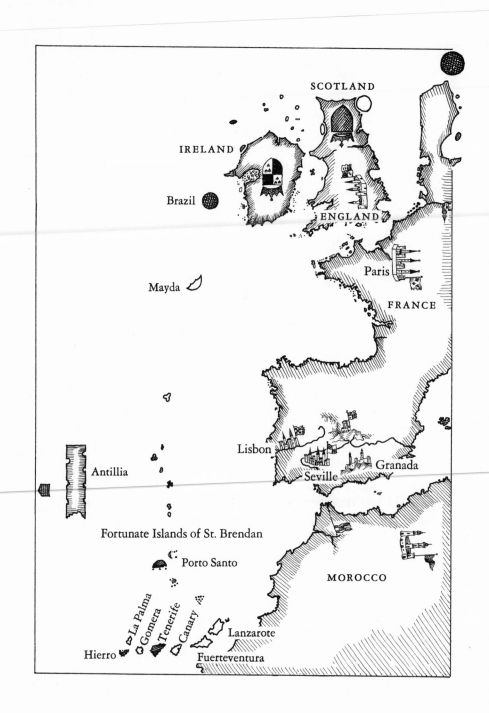

SCOTLAND

IRELAND

Brazil

ENGLAND

Mayda

Paris

FRANCE

Lisbon

Antillia

Granada

Seville

Fortunate Islands of St. Brendan

Porto Santo

MOROCCO

La Palma
Gomera
Tenerife
Canary

Lanzarote

Hierro

Fuerteventura

Brendan visited it. Canary Islanders thought they saw a mysterious island to the west, regularly, once a year, like an oasis appearing in the desert (it was, in fact, a mirage) and sent out expeditions to find it until 1721. Maps depicted the elusive "St. Brendan's Island" in unexplored areas of the Atlantic throughout the Renaissance.

Among the wonders found in the anonymous tenth century Latin *Navigatio* are a Crystal Palace (an iceberg), an Island of Small Dark Fiends (Eskimos), a Curdled Sea, (the Sargasso?) a hostile whale, a griffin, talking birds, etc. The selection below, from the *Navigatio*, describes the Island of Sheep, a whale mistaken for an island, an encounter with demons, and the arrival at the Land Promised to the Saints.

St. Brendan, the holy man, was a monk, and born in Ireland, and there he was abbot of an house. . . . There came to him an holy abbot that [was called] Barinthus. . . . And St. Brendan . . . [said], "Ye come hither for to be joyful with me. . . . Tell me what marvels ye have seen in the great Sea Ocean."

Barinthus describes how one of his monks sailed to the Land Promised to the Saints, a "fair island," with trees and herbs and "many precious stones shining bright."

And then St. Brendan purposed soon after for to seek that place by God's help, and anon began to purvey for a good ship, and a strong, and victualed it for seven years; and then he took his leave of all his brethren, and took twelve monks with him. . . .

And when St. Brendan with his twelve monks

were entered into the ship, there came other two of his monks, and prayed him that they might sail with him. And then he said,

"Ye may sail with me, but one of you shall go to hell, [before] ye come again."

But . . . they would go with him. . . .

And . . . they . . . sailed a long time . . . till at the last . . . they saw far from them a full fair island, full of green pastures, wherein were the whitest and greatest sheep that ever they saw; for every sheep was as great as an ox. And soon after came to them a goodly old man, which welcomed them, and . . . said,

"This is the Island of Sheep, and here is never cold weather, but ever summer, and that causeth the sheep to be so great and white; they eat of the best grass and herbs that is anywhere." . . .

And then they sailed forth, and . . . went upon an island . . . and made thereon a fire for to [prepare] their dinner. . . . And when the fire was right hot . . . then this island began to move; whereof the monks were afraid, and fled anon to the ship. . . . And St. Brendan comforted them, and said that it was a great fish [whale] named Jasconius, which laboreth night and day to put his tail in his mouth, but for greatness he may not.

And then . . . they sailed west three days and three nights [before] they saw any land, wherefore they were right heavy.

St. Brendan arrives at an island of talking birds—fallen angels in reality. One of them tells him that "in the end of the seventh year ye shall come into the Land of [Promise]." They visit a number of other islands, returning each year to keep the Easter Service of the Resurrection on the back of Jasconius, the friendly whale.

And then there came a south wind and drove the ship northward, where as they saw an island full dark and full of stench and smoke; and there they heard great blowing and blasting of bellows . . . [and] great thundering, whereof they were sore afraid. . . .

And soon there came a great number of fiends and assailed them with hooks and burning iron [hammers], [who] ran [into] the water, following fast their ship . . . and threw their hooks and [hammers] at them.

And they then were sore afraid, and prayed to God for . . . help; for they saw the fiends all about the ship, and . . . all the island and the sea [seemed] to be on . . . fire. And with a sorrowful cry all the fiends departed from them. . . . And then St. Brendan told to them that this was a part of hell. . . .

And then came the south wind and drove them farther into the north, where they saw an hill all on fire. . . . And then one of his monks began to cry and weep full sore, and said . . . that he might abide no longer in the ship, and anon he leaped out . . . into the sea . . . cursing the time that he was born . . . "for now I must go to perpetual pain." And then the saying of St. Brendan was verified that he said to him when he entered into the ship.

St. Brendan comes to Judas, clinging to a rock in the stormy sea, and then to an island inhabited by Paul, a 140-year-old hermit covered with bright silver hair like a Christmas tree under tinsel. Paul gives St. Brendan directions for completing his voyage to the Land of Promise.

They took their ship and sailed east forty days, and at the forty days' end it began to hail right fast, and therewith came a dark mist. . . . Soon after, that mist passed away, and anon they saw the fairest country eastward that any man might see . . . so clear and bright that it was an heavenly sight to behold; and all the trees were charged with ripe fruit and herbs full of flowers.

In [this] land they walked forty days, but they could see [no] end of that land; and there was always day and never night, and the land . . . [neither] too hot [nor] too cold. And at the last they came to a river, but they durst not go over. And there came to them a fair young man, and welcomed them . . . and said to them,

"Be ye now joyful, for this is the land that ye have sought; but our Lord will that ye depart hence hastily, and . . . that ye load your ship with the fruit of this land. . . . Thou shalt sail again into thine own country, and soon after thou comest home thou shalt die.

"And this water that thou seest here departeth the world asunder; for on that other side of the water may no man come that is in this life. . . . [But] he that keepeth our Lord's [commands] at all times shall see this land, [before] he pass out of this world."

And then St. Brendan and his monks took of that fruit as much as they would, and also took with them great plenty of precious stones . . . and went to ship, weeping sore because they might no longer abide there.

And then they took their ship and came home into Ireland in safety, whom their brethren received with great joy, giving thankings to our Lord, which had kept them all those seven years from many a peril.

ANTILLIA AND THE SEVEN BISHOPS

When Arab armies with flashing scimitars routed the forces of King Roderick in 711, and overran the Spanish peninsula, a band of refugees led by seven bishops is supposed to have fled across the Ocean Sea to an island called "Antillia." Here each bishop was said to have founded a city for his congregation, and legend related that the island became a Utopia, where poverty and violence were unknown.

This "most picturesque and adventurous of legends" explains the presence of box-shaped "Antillia" on many fifteenth century maps. It is the only imaginary island connected with a real historical event. Ferdinand Columbus said Antillia was over 600 miles west of the Azores, while the Florentine geographer Toscanelli used it as a landmark for measuring the distance between Lisbon and Japan.

"From the island Antillia, which you call the 'Island of the Seven Cities,' to the very noble island of Cipangu are . . . 2,500 miles," Toscanelli wrote a Portuguese friend in 1474.

(A sixteenth century mapmaker placed the "seven cities" in North America, however, scattering seven miters to represent them from Newfoundland to Florida.)

Antillia, like the islands of St. Brendan, may be a ghost of Plato's lost Atlantis. Early writers tried to derive the name "Antillia" from "Atlantis." Later writers connected it with Latin *anterior:* Antillia was the island one reached *before* (anterior to) Japan. Another derivation relates the name to an Arab phrase meaning "Dragon's Isle."

We know about Antillia only from early maps and brief notices in early histories. The selections below consist of a description of the island from Martin Behaim's Globe (1492), the oldest globe in the world today; and an account by Ferdinand Columbus, in his *Life of the Admiral Christopher Columbus* (1571), of a mysterious voyage Prince Henry the Navigator's seamen are said to have made to Antillia, perhaps about 1430.

In the year [714] of Christ, when the whole of Spain had been won by the heathen (Moors) of Africa, the above island Antillia, called *Septe citade* (Seven Cities), was inhabited by an archbishop from the Porto in Portugal, with six other bishops, and other Christians, men and women, who had fled thither from Spain, by ship, together with their cattle, belongings, and goods. [In] 1414 a ship from

Spain got nighest it without being endangered.
                    (*Martin Behaim's Globe*, 1492)

[The Portuguese] hold it for certain that [Antillia] is the Island of the Seven Cities, settled by the Portuguese at the time the Moors conquered Spain from King Rodrigo [Roderick], that is, in the year A.D. 714. They saw that at that time seven bishops embarked from Spain and came with their ships and people to this island, where each founded a city; and in order that their people might give up all thought of returning to Spain they burned their ships, riggings, and all else needed for navigation. Some Portuguese who speculated about this island conjectured that many of their nation had gone thither but were never able to return.

In particular they say that in the time of the Infante Dom Henrique of Portugal [Prince Henry the Navigator] there arrived at this island of Antillia a Portuguese ship, driven there by a storm. After coming ashore, the ship's people were conducted by the inhabitants of the island to their church to see if the visitors were Christians and observed the rites of the Catholic religion. Satisfied that they were Christians, the islanders prayed the ship's people not to leave before the return of their absent lord, whom they would immediately notify of the ship's arrival. They also said that their lord would do great honor to the visitors and give them many presents.

But the ship's master and the sailors feared to be detained, reasoning that because these people did not wish to be known abroad they might burn their ship. So they left for Portugal with their news, expecting to be rewarded by the Infante [Prince Henry], who instead rebuked them severely and ordered them to return immediately to the island; but the master took fright and escaped from Portugal with his ship and crew.

It is said that while the sailors were in the church on that island the ship's boys gathered sand for the firebox and found that it was one third fine gold.

(*Ferdinand Columbus*, The Life of the
Admiral Christopher Columbus, *1571*)

THE MEDIEVAL WORLD OF MARVELS

While mapmakers sprinkled the Atlantic with imaginary islands, medieval geographers provided accounts of the Island of Earth (the *orbis terrarum*) and its surrounding Ocean Sea that were mixtures of fact and fiction. One of the most fictitious, but most entertaining, was John Mandeville's *Travels* (1360–62).

Mandeville's *Travels* was one of the most popular books of the Middle Ages. It was supposed to be a guide for pilgrims to Jerusalem, also an autobiographical narrative of Mandeville's trips there. But when the author reached the Holy Land, he kept going—to India, Cathay, and near the Earthly Paradise. On the way he encountered or heard about Amazons, men with huge "umbrella feet," ants which dug for gold, one-eyed cyclops, men whose heads were tucked beneath their shoulders, weeping crocodiles, and many other fantastic creatures. He described a number of mythical islands in the Ocean Sea.

Mandeville may have visited Palestine and Egypt, but he did the rest of his traveling comfortably seated in an armchair before his fire in Liège, Belgium. That is, he "borrowed" the material for most of his book from writings of Friar Odoric, John de Plano Carpini, and Marco Polo—authentic explorers of Asia—and from encyclopedic works like Vincent of Beauvais's *Speculum Mundi.*

Yet this kindly, curious English physician had a vivid imagination, a gift for storytelling that enabled him to improve what he copied. His book was so readable that it was soon translated from its original French into the chief languages of western Europe. Its descriptions of Amazons, the Earthly Paradise, and the Fountain of Youth (of which Mandeville said he drank) led early explorers to look for these wonders.

Mandeville has sometimes been considered as fictitious as his book. But it is now believed that there was an Englishman of that name who was the author of the famous *Travels.* The deathbed confession Mandeville is said to have made in 1372 is accepted: that when he was a young man he had killed a count and been forced to flee from England, and that he practiced medicine at Liège—where he was known as "Master John with the Beard"—from 1343 on.

The selections below describe Amazons, dragons beyond Thule, and the Earthly Paradise, but also include a proof that the world is round. In spite of his appetite for marvels, Mandeville, who had studied at the University of Paris, was in advance of many geographers in believing that you could sail around the world, as Magellan's men later did, and in considering the entire earth habitable.

Amazons

Beside Chaldea is the land of Amazon . . . an isle, closed all about with water . . . which we call the maiden land or the land of women. . . . There . . . [the women] never let men dwell with them over seven days, [nor] never suffer [boy] child be nourished among them.

But, when they will have fellowship of men, they draw them [beyond the water, to another] land where their [sweethearts] dwell, and there they dwell with them eight or nine days, and then wend home again. And if any of them be with child and have a son, they keep it till it can speak and [walk] and eat by itself and then send it to the father or else slay it. And if it be a maiden child, they [rear it and train it to use sword and shield, or bow and arrows].

There is evermore in that realm a queen that has the governance of the land, and . . . her they are all obeying. And this queen is evermore chosen by election, for they choose her that is doughtiest in arms.

These women are noble warriors and wise; and therefore kings of other realms nigh them [pay] them for to help them in their wars.

Amazons were first described by the ancient Greeks, the historian Herodotus locating them on the shores of the Black Sea. In 1541 a Spaniard thought he saw them fighting against his forces along the banks of the largest river in South America, and therefore named the river *Rio de las Amazonas* (the Amazon).

The Earthly Paradise

Beyond these isles [islands east of Ceylon], toward the east, is yet another isle that is called Thule [Iceland]; and it is the furthest isle of the world inhabited with men. Of this isle speaks the poet [Virgil] and says, *Tibi serviet ultima Thule,* "To thee [Augustus Caesar]," he says, "shall serve Thule, the furthest isle of the world."

At the yonder side of this isle, toward the east, runs a great water, beyond the which is nought but waste land and wilderness. In that wilderness is nothing dwelling but dragons and other wild beasts, cruel and fell. . . .

Beyond these isles that I have told you of [islands east of Ceylon] and the deserts of the lordship of Prester John [near Korea], to go even east, is no land inhabited . . . but wastes and wildernesses. . . . And that murk land and those deserts last right to Paradise terrestrial, wherein Adam and Eve were put. . . . And that place is toward the east at the beginning of the earth.

But that is not our east, where the sun rises [for] us; for, when the sun rises in those countries, then is it midnight in our country, because of the roundness of the earth. For . . . God made the earth all round in midst of the firmament. . . .

Of Paradise can I not speak properly, for I have not been there. . . . But [as much] as I have heard of wise men . . . I will tell you.

Paradise terrestrial . . . is the highest land of the world . . . so high that it touches near to the circle of the moon. For it is so high that Noah's flood might not come thereto, which flood covered all the earth but it. Paradise is closed all about with a wall; but whereof the wall is made, can no man tell. It is . . . covered so with moss and with brush that men may see no stone. . . . The wall of Paradise stretches from the south toward the north; and there is none entry open into it, because of fire evermore burning, the which is called the flaming sword that God ordained there before the entry. . . .

In the midst of Paradise is a well out of the which there come four floods, that run through divers lands. These floods sink down into the earth within Paradise and run so under the earth many a mile, and afterwards come they up again out of the earth in far countries.

The first of these floods which is called Phison or Ganges, springs up in India . . . and runs eastward through India into the great sea Ocean. In that river are many precious stones and great plenty of the tree that is called *lignum aloes,* and [much] gravel of gold. This river is called . . . Ganges for a king that was in India. . . .

The second river is called Nilus or Gyon; and it

rises up out of the earth, a little from Mount Atlas. And not far thence it sinks down again into the earth . . . till it comes at the Red Sea bank, and there it rises up again . . . and runs all about Ethiopia, and so through Egypt . . . [to] Great Alexandria, and there . . . into the sea Mediterranean. This river is evermore troubled and therefore is it called Gyon. . . .

The third river is called Tigris, that is to say Fast Running . . . after a beast that has the same name and . . . is the swiftest beast of foot of the world. This river begins in Armenia . . . and runs so through Armenia and Asia toward the south . . . into the sea Mediterranean.

The fourth river is called Euphrates . . . [meaning] Well Bearing; for there grow many good things upon that river. That river runs through Media, Armenia, and Persia. . . . [Thus] all the fresh waters of the world take their beginning of the . . . well that springs up in Paradise.

And ye shall understand that no man living may go to Paradise. For by land may no man go thither because of wild beasts that are in the wilderness and for hills and rocks which no man may pass, and also for murk places, of which there are many there. By water also may no man pass thither, for those rivers come with so great a course and so great a birr and waves that no ship may go [nor] sail against them. There is also so great noise of waters that a man may not hear another, cry he never so high.

Mandeville thought of Jerusalem as at the center of the earth, with the Earthly Paradise so far east of Jerusalem as to be almost opposite it. In passages like the one above, he seems to accept the theory of certain geographers that the earth is not perfectly round but slightly pear-shaped, with the Earthly Paradise at its highest point.

The World Is Round

And ye shall understand that in this land [Sumatra] . . . men may not see the star that is called *Polus Articus,* which stands even north and stirs never, by which shipmen are led, for it is not seen in the south. But there is another star which is called Antarctic . . . and by that star are shipmen led there, as shipmen are led here by *Polus Articus.* And right as that star may not be seen here . . . this star may not be seen there.

And thereby may men see well that the world is all round; for parts of the firmament which may be seen in some country may not be seen in another. . . . For I have been in Brabant and seen by the astrolabe that the Pole Arctic is there 53 degrees high and in Almayne [Germany] toward Bohemia it has 58 degrees, and furthermore toward the north it has 62 degrees of height. . . . Afterward I went toward the south and I found that in Libya [Africa] see men first the star Antarctic; and as I went farther [south], I found that in high Libya it has in height 18 degrees and some minutes. . . .

And therefore I say . . . that a man might go all

the world about, both above and beneath, and come again to his own country, so that he had his health, good shipping, and good company. . . . And alway he should find men, lands, isles and cities and towns, as are in their countries.

Mandeville is ahead of other geographers in considering the Frigid and Torrid zones habitable. His proof of the roundness of the world—that as you travel north or south familiar stars disappear and new ones take their places—is drawn from Aristotle.

Chapter Two

THE VIKING
RECONNAISSANCE

By God's will, after a long voyage from the island of Greenland to the south toward the most distant remaining parts of the western ocean sea, sailing southward amidst the ice, . . . Bjarni and Leif Ericson discovered a new land, extemely fertile and even having vines, the which island they named Vinland.

—The Vinland Map and the Tartar Relation

The first announcement of the finding of Vinland by the Norsemen was buried in a Latin church history, written by a German schoolmaster named Adam of Bremen. It is as though news of a landing on the moon appeared first in the minutes of a local PTA meeting!

Adam of Bremen had talked to King Svein Estridson of Denmark while collecting material for his *History of the Archbishopric of Hamburg*. King Svein, who loved to listen to Icelandic poets and saga-tellers, passed on to Adam the information that the Norse had recently added still another to their string of bases stretching west across the Ocean Sea: an "island" where grapes grew wild.

The selection below, from Adam of Bremen's *History of the Archbishopric of Hamburg* (written around 1070), is the first authentic mention in world literature of the North American continent.

Moreover he [Svein Estridson, King of Denmark 1047–1076] spoke of an island in that ocean discovered by many, which is called Vinland, for the reason that vines grow wild there, which yield the best of wine. Moreover that grain unsown grows there abundantly, is not a fabulous fancy, but, from the accounts of the Danes, we know to be a fact.

Beyond this island, it is said, that there is no habitable land in that ocean, but all those regions which are beyond are filled with insupportable ice and boundless gloom, to which Martian [Martianus Capella, fifth-century geographer] thus refers: "One day's sail beyond Thule the sea is frozen." This was

essayed not long since by that very enterprising
Northmen's prince, Harold [Haardraade, King of
Norway, 1047–1066], who explored the extent of
the northern ocean with his ship, but was scarcely
able by retreating to escape in safety from the gulf's
enormous abyss, where before his eyes the vanishing
bounds of earth were hidden in gloom.

AN UNKNOWN SHORE

After Adam of Bremen, there were only a few brief references to Vinland in Icelandic histories—but the Icelandic
sagas gave complete accounts of the voyages there.

"Saga" means "that which is said." The sagas were
stories, handed down by word of mouth, of the famous
deeds of Icelanders. Iceland was a country of proud,
fiercely independent families who had emigrated from
Norway because they did not wish to be ruled by the king
of Norway. These families governed themselves and kept
their traditions alive by composing sagas about notable
happenings.

There were several kinds of sagas. The "family sagas"
for the most part reported facts, like newspapers. So did
the sagas of the Norwegian kings. The "lying" or "stepmother" sagas, on the other hand, added a few marvels to
the authentic history they presented. One of the two sagas
which describe the Norse voyages to Vinland, the Karlsevni Saga, is a family saga, while the other, the Greenland
Saga, is a "stepmother" saga—but the two versions agree
on many points. These sagas were written down in the
thirteenth century but were originally composed two hundred years earlier.

According to the Greenland Saga, Vinland was first

sighted not by Leif Ericson but by Bjarni Herjulfson, an Icelander whose father had migrated to Greenland. Bjarni was a "modern" Viking, that is, one of the capable merchant Vikings who had succeeded the first looters. His voyage apparently received confirmation in 1965 from the discovery of the fifteenth century Vinland Map, which not only shows Vinland but contains a notation stating that Bjarni and Leif Ericson both sailed there. However, some scholars question the map's authenticity.

The selection below, from the Greenland Saga, describes Bjarni's historic voyage, made in A.D. 986.

Bjarni [Herjulfson] was a talented fellow and from early youth his thoughts had turned to the sea. His trading voyages won him wealth and honor; before long he mastered a ship of his own. He made it his custom to live with his father in Iceland one winter and sail abroad the next.

During the last winter that Bjarni was in Norway [on a visit], his father Herjulf broke up their home in Iceland and prepared to leave for Greenland with Eric the Red [A.D. 986]. Aboard Herjulf's ship there was a Christian man from the Hebrides, and he made a poem on the trip that was known as "The Song of the Breakers." One verse ran as follows:

> I pray our Christ will bless this voyage,
> The faultless One, who tests His servants;
> He rules the vaulted halls of heaven;
> May He extend His hand o'er us!

Herjulf settled at Herjulfsness [Greenland] and was held in the greatest respect.

That summer Bjarni sailed to Eyrar in Iceland only to find that his father had left in the spring. This news affected Bjarni a good deal, and he would not even trouble to unload his ship. His men asked him what he had in mind, and he answered that he planned to spend the winter with his father as he had always done—"and if you will go with me, I shall steer straight for Greenland." They all agreed to do as he thought best.

Then Bjarni said, "People will call us fools for starting off on this voyage—we who have never been in the Greenland seas!"

In spite of this, they put to sea as soon as they could get ready and sailed for three days. There was then no land in sight, the fair wind died down, and they were beset by fogs and north winds until they lost all track of their course. This went on for many days, and then the sun came out again, so they could get their bearings.

They hoisted sail and sailed all day before they sighted land. They wondered what country this might be, but it was Bjarni's opinion that it could not be Greenland. They asked him, was he going to land, but he said, "It is my advice that we only skirt the shore." As they did so, they found that the land was not mountainous but covered with small wooded knolls.

They left the land behind on their port side, with the sheet pointed toward the shore. They sailed for two days and found another country. They asked

Bjarni if he thought that this would be Greenland, but he replied that this was no more Greenland than the other one, "for in Greenland there are said to be huge glaciers." As they approached the shore, they saw that it was a level country and well wooded. The wind died down and the crew insisted that they ought to land, but Bjarni refused. The men claimed that they were short of wood and water.

"You have no lack of either," said Bjarni, but at this the men grumbled a good deal. He told them to hoist sail, and then they steered the ship away from shore.

For three days they sailed with a southwesterly breeze before they caught sight of a third coast. This country had many high mountains topped with glaciers. Again they asked Bjarni if he was going to land, and again he said no, "for this country looks pretty worthless to me." This time they did not even furl their sail but steered along the coast and found that it was an island. Again they left the country astern and sailed away in the same direction. A storm blew up and Bjarni told his crew to reef the sail and not to press on any faster than their ship and her tackle could bear.

They sailed for four days and then they found a fourth country. Again they asked Bjarni if he thought this was Greenland, and Bjarni answered, "This is most like what I have been told about Greenland, and here we shall try to land."

So that evening they made their way to a jutting headland. On the cape they found a boat, and it was the very cape on which Herjulf, Bjarni's father, had settled and to which he had given his name, so that it has since been known as Herjulfsness.

Bjarni now went to his father's house and from this time on he sailed no more.

LEIF THE LUCKY

Leif Ericson, a tall, strong young Viking who had a "noble and generous" nature, was driven to Vinland by a storm while on his way back to Greenland from Norway. His father, Eric the Red (probably so named because of his red hair) had been the first to explore Greenland.

When banished from Iceland by his enemies, Eric had reconnoitered the bleak, glacier-capped country farther west and given it its appealing—and inaccurate—name to attract settlers. In spite of Greenland's lack of wood and iron, and the fact that grain would not grow in its severe climate, Eric founded a successful colony of three thousand persons there. He was a crusty old pagan whose determination rubbed off on his son.

As a young man, Leif Ericson set sail for Norway to seek riches. Two storms made this a memorable voyage. The first blew him off his course into a love affair in the Hebrides Islands near Scotland. Then, on his return voyage from Norway, A.D. 1000, as he attempted to steer straight for Greenland without making the usual stopover at Iceland, the second storm blew him to North America.

Leif Ericson's ship was probably not a Viking "longship" but a merchant *knorr*—a shorter, sturdier vessel with high freeboard and wide bottom. These ships were seaworthy in the Atlantic rollers, capable of making long ocean voyages carrying thirty or forty people, livestock, and provisions. (A replica of a famous Viking ship unearthed at Gokstad, Norway, crossed the Atlantic in 1893 in twenty-eight days without trouble.)

A knorr might be 60 to 70 feet long. It was driven by oars and a large, square sail raised on a 30-foot mast. The ship was "clinker-built," that is, with the edges of the upper planks projecting over the lower. It was steered by an oar, the "steerboard," attached to the right side at the stern. Both sail and ship's sides were brightly painted.

Both prow and stern of a Viking vessel curved up in a carved gilt sea serpent's head. This head, with its glaring eyes and terrifying expression, was supposed to frighten evil spirits away. Pagan religious belief required that it be removed when the ship approached its home port, lest the head frighten good spirits on land. As the Vikings neared home they hung their shields, painted alternately black and yellow, from the gunwales, the gold ornaments of the ship shone like fire in the sun, and the vessel, which the Norse poets called "steed of the waves," made a gala appearance.

The selection below, from the Karlsevni Saga, describes Leif Ericson's arrival in Vinland, in A.D. 1000.

Eric the Red lived at Brattahlid [Greenland], where he was held in the highest respect and deferred to by all. Eric's children were Leif, Thorvald, Thorstein, and a daughter named Freydis. . . .

One summer [A.D. 999] Eric's son Leif sailed for Norway to visit the court of King Olaf Trygvason. On his way from Greenland he was blown out of his course and landed on the Hebrides, off the west coast

of Scotland. The winds kept blowing contrary for a
long time, and he had to stay there most of the
summer.

Here Leif grew fond of a woman named Thorgunna. She was of good family and, as Leif discovered, not without some knowledge of secret lore.
When Leif was making ready to sail, Thorgunna
begged to be taken along. Leif asked if this would
be agreeable to her family, but she said that made no
difference. Leif, however, refused to carry off a
woman of her high rank in a strange country where,
as he said, "we are so few in number."

"Someday," said Thorgunna, "you may regret
that you chose this course."

"I shall have to risk that," retorted Leif. . . .

When he left, Leif gave her a gold ring, a home-
spun Greenland mantle, and a belt of walrus tusk.
. . . Leif now sailed away from the Hebrides and got
to Norway by fall. He sought the court of King Olaf
Trygvason, and entered his service. The king showed
Leif great favor, for it seemed to him that Leif was
a fine, well-bred man.

One time he called Leif in and asked him, "Are
you planning to sail out to Greenland this summer?"

"I am," answered Leif, "if it is not against your
will."

"Indeed," said the king, "I am anxious that you
should. You shall go with a special mission from me:
to proclaim Christianity in Greenland."

Leif said he would do as the king wished, but added that it might not be an easy mission to accomplish in Greenland. The king insisted, however, that he knew no man better fitted for it than Leif.

"And I am confident," he added, "that fortune will smile on you."

"That will only be," said Leif, "if your good luck is added to mine."

Leif sailed as soon as he could get ready, and was blown around a great deal. He hit upon countries he had not expected to see. There he found self-sown wheat fields and grapevines, and a tree called *mosur* [possibly bird's-eye maple], and he brought with him samples of all these. Some of the timber was big enough to use in building houses.

Leif found some shipwrecked men and took them home with him and gave them all lodgings for the winter. He showed so noble and generous a nature —in bringing Christianity to Greenland and in rescuing these men—that after this he was called Leif the Lucky.

Leif landed in Ericsfjord and made his way home to Brattahlid [Greenland], where he was well received.

TYRKER FINDS GRAPES

Wine in gold and silver cups warmed the hearts of the Vikings through the long winters, but most of them had never seen the purple grapes growing on the vine. When

Leif Ericson voyaged to North America in 1002, a German crewman named Tyrker found wild grapes and excitedly identified them for his comrades.

Leif then named the great "island" he had reached "Vinland" or "Wineland." The name would suggest a northern earthly paradise to the thirsty Vikings and might attract future settlers.

Where was Vinland?

The first land Leif Ericson sighted was a stony, unprofitable shore whose high mountains were crowned with glaciers. These glaciers might have been merely snowcaps. Leif called the land Helluland (Land of Flat Rocks), and most scholars identify it with Labrador.

The second land Leif came to had broad beaches and a low-lying, wooded shore. He named it Markland (Forest Land)—perhaps Nova Scotia, with its long, unbroken coast.

Finally, Leif Ericson and his crew arrived at a country which had no mountains at all, but lovely wooded knolls and groves, sandy beaches, many islands and great shallows in the sea—a land of "self-sown wheat" and wild grapes and bright sunshine. As Leif stared landward, the sea and sky and frothy surf breaking on the beaches were like a blue-and-white engraving.

This beautiful country had salmon swimming in its offshore waters. The Vikings found its winter climate so mild that cattle could graze in the fields. No snow fell, and they observed that the sun in midwinter (December 21) was as high in the sky here as it was at the beginning of winter (October 14) in Iceland. However, the natives, whom the Vikings contemptuously called *skraelings* ("savages"), were warlike and hostile.

Wild grapes are found as far north as Maine, wild rice

(the "self-sown wheat") as far north as Newfoundland. In Leif Ericson's time salmon were caught as far south as Delaware, but winters as mild as those described would have occurred regularly only below the Potomac River. In 1963 authentic Viking ruins *were* discovered in northern Newfoundland: the remains of nine houses with beaten earthen floors, turf walls, and fireplaces with typical Norse ember pits.

Because of the severe climate and absence of wild grapes, however, Newfoundland cannot be Vinland—unless Leif Ericson was practicing his father's salesmanship. Assuming that the sagas are truthful, we would have to look for Vinland between southern New England, where mild winters occasionally occur, and Delaware.

The following selection, from the Greenland Saga, tells of Leif Ericson's voyage of 1002. The Greenland Saga presents it as his first journey to Vinland, but if we accept the Karlsevni Saga's account of Leif's voyage of 1000, it would be his second.

People in Greenland were now eagerly talking about exploring the lands that had been seen. Leif Ericson made a visit to Bjarni Herjulfson and bought a ship from him. Then he gathered a crew of thirty-five men and asked his father Eric to lead the expedition. But Eric held back.

"I am getting along in years," he said, "and I am less able to put up with such hardships than I used to be."

But Leif insisted that he was still the ablest and the luckiest of his clan, and gradually he talked Eric into consenting. When they were ready, Eric rode

from home and got almost down to the ship. Then the horse he was riding stumbled, so he fell off and hurt his foot.

Eric then said, "It seems that I am not fated to find other lands than the one in which we are now living. We shall ride no farther together."

Eric returned to Brattahlid, while Leif went down to the ship with his thirty-five companions. One of them was a German by the name of Tyrker.

They fitted out the ship and sailed away. The first country they found was the one that Bjarni had seen last. Here they sailed to shore and dropped anchor, put out a boat and went on land. They saw no grass, the mountain tops were covered with glaciers, and from sea to mountain the country was like one slab of rock. It looked to be a barren, unprofitable country.

Then Leif remarked, "Now at least we have done better than Bjarni, who never even set foot on these shores! I am going to give the country a name, and I shall call it Helluland [land of flat rocks]."

They went on board and sailed out to sea once more. They found a second country, and again they dropped anchor, put out a boat, and went ashore. This country was level and wooded, with broad white beaches wherever they went and a gently sloping shoreline.

Leif said, "I shall give this country a name that fits with its natural character and call it Markland [forest land]." Then they hurried back to their ships and sailed on with a northeast breeze.

After two days' sail they sighted another shore and landed on an island to the north of the mainland. It was a fine, bright day, and as they looked around they discovered dew on the grass. It so happened that they picked up some of the dew in their hands and tasted of it, and it seemed to them that they had never tasted anything so sweet. Then they returned to the ship and sailed through the channel between the island and a cape jutting out to the north of the mainland.

They steered a westerly course past the cape and found great shallows at ebb tide, so that their ship was beached and lay some distance from the sea. But they were so eager to go ashore that they could not bear to wait till the tide rose under their ship. They ran up on the shore to a place where a stream flowed out of a lake. . . . Later they decided to stay there through the winter and set up large houses.

There was no lack of salmon either in the river or in the lake, and it was bigger salmon than they had ever seen. Nature was so generous here that it seemed to them no cattle would need any winter fodder but could graze outdoors. There was no frost in winter, and the grass hardly withered. The days and nights were more nearly equal than in Greenland or Iceland, and on the shortest day of the year the sun was up from breakfast time to midafternoon [as it was not in Iceland after the middle of October].

When they had finished building their houses, Leif said to his companions, "Now I am going to divide our company into two groups, for I want to get this country explored. Half the men will stay here at the camp, while the other half goes exploring. They shall not go so far that they cannot get back home by evening, and they shall stay together."

So for a time they did this, and sometimes Leif went along with the exploring party and sometimes he stayed at home. Leif was a big, strapping fellow, handsome to look at, thoughtful and temperate in all things.

One evening the news spread that a member of the crew was missing, none other than Tyrker the German. Leif was much disturbed at this, for Tyrker had lived in their household a long time and had been greatly devoted to Leif when he was a child. Leif angrily reproached his men and made ready to start off with a search party of twelve.

They had scarcely left the house when Tyrker came walking toward them, and he was received with great joy. Leif saw at once that his foster father was in high spirits. Tyrker was a short fellow, rather puny-looking, with a prominent forehead and restless eyes in a smallish face; but he was handy at all sorts of craftsmanship.

Leif said to him, "Why were you so late, foster father, and how did you get parted from your company?"

Tyrker first talked a long time in German, rolled his eyes and made faces. They did not understand a word he said. After a while he changed over and spoke Norse.

"I did not go far beyond the rest of you, and yet I have some real news for you. I found grapevines and grapes!"

"Is this really true, foster father mine?" said Leif.

"Certainly it is true," he answered, "for I was born where there is no lack either of vines or grapes."

Now they slept that night, but the next morning Leif told his crew, "From now on we have two jobs on our hands. On one day we shall gather grapes, and on the next we shall cut grapevines and chop down the trees to make a cargo for my ship."

So they followed this plan, and it is said that they loaded up the afterboat with grapes, and the ship itself with a cargo of timber. When spring came, they made the ship ready and sailed away. Leif gave this country a name to suit its resources: he called it Vinland [wine land].

CAPE CROSSNESS

The Vikings sailed west not merely for the sake of adventure but in hopes of gain. After the voyages of Bjarni Herjulfson and Leif Ericson, according to the sagas, "people were talking of the journey to Vinland, for this seemed an open road to wealth and honor."

Thorvald, one of Leif's brothers, tried his luck in 1004. He was looking for *landskostir*—resources. He wanted to find products he could sell back in Greenland, such as grapes and wood, or fertile land he could settle.

One obstacle stood between the Norse colonists and the riches they dreamed of: the North American Indian, his face daubed with war paint. At first the "skraelings" bartered valuable beaver skins and fine furs for cheap red cloth. Later, sensing that the Vikings were not paying a fair price for their goods, the Indians became hostile. With arrows, darts, lances, wooden clubs and slings, the skraelings swarmed down upon the Vikings. A springy pole catapulted huge stones against the intruders.

The Vikings met the onslaught with round linden-wood shields, steel swords, and battle-axes. With these weapons they might win a skirmish, but could not permanently gain the upper hand. Only firearms would have enabled them to hold off the much more numerous skraelings and enlarge their foothold.

"Even though the country was richly endowed by nature, they [the Vikings] would always live in dread and turmoil because of the enmity of those who lived there before," commented the Karlsevni Saga.

The following selection, from the Greenland Saga, describes Thorvald's expedition. Its tragic ending was a dark omen for the future.

People kept talking a great deal about Leif's voyage to Vinland, and his brother Thorvald maintained that the country was still too scantily explored.

Leif spoke to him and said, "If you are burning

to see Vinland, brother, you are welcome to my ship. . . ."

Then Thorvald got ready for the voyage with a crew of thirty men, consulting all the time with his brother Leif. They fixed up the ship and sailed away, and nothing is reported to have happened before they got to Vinland. At Leif's camp they laid up their ship and spent the winter, getting their food by fishing.

In the spring Thorvald told his men to get the ship ready. He sent some of them out with the after-boat and asked them to spend the summer exploring the coast to the west. They found that it was a lovely, wooded country, and that the woods ran almost down to the sea, with a white, sandy beach. The sea was full of islands and great shallows. Nowhere did they find any vestiges of men or animals, except a wooden granary on one of the islands to the west. They found no other human product, and in the fall they turned back to Leif's camp.

In the second summer Thorvald sailed his vessel eastward and along the coast to the north. As they were rounding a certain cape, a stiff storm fell upon them and drove them on shore, so that their keel was broken and they had to stay there a long time while they repaired the ship.

Then Thorvald said to his men, "I wish we might raise up the keel on this cape and call the cape Keelness," and so they did.

Then they sailed along the coast to the east, into some nearby fjord mouths, and headed for a jutting cape that rose high out of the sea and was all covered with woods. Here they anchored the ship and laid down a gangplank to the shore. Thorvald went ashore with all his company.

Then he said, "This is beautiful, and here I should like to build me a home."

After a time they went back to the ship. Then they caught sight of three little mounds on the sand farther in on the cape. When they got closer to them, they saw three skin-covered boats, with three men under each. They split up their force and seized all the men but one, who escaped in his boat. They killed all eight of them, and then returned to the cape. Here they saw a number of mounds in the fjord and guessed that these must be human dwelling places.

After that such a drowsiness fell upon them that they simply could not stay awake, and they all fell asleep. Then a voice cried out to them, so that they all awoke, and this is what the voice said: "Wake up, Thorvald, and all your crew, if you value your lives! Get aboard the ship with your men and hurry away from this country with all speed!"

A host of boats was then heading toward them from the inner end of the fjord.

Thorvald then said, "We shall set up our breast-works on both sides of the ship and defend ourselves as best we can, but do as little killing as possible." So they did, and after the savages had shot at them for a while, they hurried away as fast as they could.

Thorvald asked if any of his men were wounded. They said they were not.

"I have got a wound under my arm," he said; "an arrow flew between the gunwale and my shield and struck me under the arm, and here is the arrow. This will be the last of me. Now I advise you to make ready for your return as quickly as possible. But me you shall take back to that cape which I found so inviting. It looks as if I spoke the truth without knowing it when I said that I might live there some-day! Bury me there with a cross at my head and another at my feet, and ever after you shall call it Crossness."

So Thorvald died and they did everything just as he had told them. Then they came back to their companions and exchanged news about all that had happened. They spent the winter there and gathered grapes and vines for the ship.

The next spring they sailed back to Greenland and steered the ship into Ericsfjord and had plenty of news to tell Leif.

After Thorvald's death, an Icelandic merchant named Karlsevni took a well-equipped fleet of three ships and 160 men into the Gulf of St. Lawrence and then down the New England coast, but failed to establish a colony because of the bitter enmity of the Indians (1010–13). In Streamfjord (probably New Brunswick, Canada) the first white baby to be born in North America arrived, and was named Snorri. Then Freydis, the adventurous but cruel sister of Leif Ericson, caused much strife on a briefer expedition (1014–15).

But the Vikings had overextended themselves by sailing west to Vinland. After 1015 only two other journeys to North America are mentioned. In 1121 (or 1117) a bishop "sought Vinland"—whether or not he reached it is unknown; and in 1347 a vessel brought a cargo of wood to Iceland from Markland. Indians, probably of the Iroquois or Algonquin tribes, had forced these first European colonists to leave the new lands.

Thus the Viking voyages resulted in a daring reconnaissance but not a settlement.

Because Europe was poor, divided into numerous warring petty kingdoms, and lacking in both political organization and accumulated capital, it could not take advantage of the Viking discoveries. The Vikings themselves did not guess the dimensions of their westernmost "island." In the later Middle Ages they lost even their Greenland colonies, through malnutrition and Eskimo attacks. (Norway, ravaged by the Black Death in 1349, had entered into a union with Denmark and Sweden in 1397, and after that became less and less interested in her Atlantic settlements.)

Nevertheless the voyages of Bjarni Herjulfson, Leif Ericson, and others across icy seas to North America remain among the heroic events of Western history. Although they had not read Plato, they touched the shores of his "boundless continent." While other mariners shrank from the Green Sea of Darkness and sailed in sight of familiar coasts, the Vikings were exploring bays and headlands three thousand miles from Europe. They were the first American pioneers.

Chapter Three

~o

THE ENTERPRISE
OF THE INDIES

By these presents we send the nobleman Christopher
Columbus through the ocean seas with three
equipped caravels, to the regions of India. . . .
                    —Passport of Christopher Columbus

Two thousand years after Plato's fable of Atlantis, five hundred years after the Norse reconnaissance, came the real beginning of European expansion overseas. In a copy of Seneca's *Tragedies* in the Columbus Library of Seville, beneath Seneca's famous prophecy that one day "new worlds" would be discovered beyond Iceland, is a proud note in the handwriting of Columbus's son Ferdinand:

Haec profetia impleta est per patrem meum . . . almirantem anno 1492—"This prophecy was fulfilled through my father . . . the Admiral, in the year 1492."

No painter made a portrait of Columbus during his lifetime. But the devoted Ferdinand, the son of Columbus and Beatriz Enríquez de Harana, remedied this omission by describing not only Columbus's physical appearance but also his mental traits. Ferdinand had sailed with his father on the fourth voyage to the West Indies, but later settled down as a scholar in Seville, in a house with a large garden planted with trees and shrubs from the Caribbean.

Ferdinand's sketch is complemented by one by Bishop Las Casas, the "Apostle to the Indies." Young Bartolomé de Las Casas had gone out to the West Indies in 1500 to seek his fortune; instead, among the greedy Spanish gold hunters and mistreated Indians, he found the compassion of Christ. He became the first priest ordained in the Western Hemisphere, and spent the rest of his life fighting to protect the Indians from slavery. He criticized Columbus sharply for his policy toward the Indians, but praised him as a man who endured "innumerable difficulties . . . and dangers" in order to bring Christianity to new lands.

The selections below are from Ferdinand Columbus's *Life of the Admiral Christopher Columbus* (1571) and Las Casas' *Historia de las Indias*, written 1527–63 but considered too "controversial" to publish until 1875.

The Admiral was a well-built man of more than average stature, the face long, the cheeks somewhat high, his body neither fat nor lean. He had an aquiline nose and light-colored eyes; his complexion too was light and tending to bright red. In youth his hair was blond, but when he reached the age of thirty, it all turned white.

In eating and drinking, and in the adornment of his person, he was very moderate and modest. He was affable in conversation with strangers and very pleasant to the members of his household, though with a certain gravity.

He was so strict in matters of religion that for fasting and saying prayers he might have been taken for a member of a religious order. He was so great an enemy of swearing and blasphemy that I give my word I never heard him utter any other oath than "By St. Ferdinand!" and when he grew very angry with someone, his rebuke was to say "God take you!" for doing or saying that.

If he had to write anything, he always began by writing these words: *Iesus cum Maria sit nobis in via* ["Jesus and Mary be with us on our journey"]. And so fine was his hand that he might have earned his bread by that skill alone.

(*Ferdinand Columbus*)

He was gracious and cheerful in speaking and . . . eloquent and boastful in his transactions. . . .

When some gold or precious things were brought to him, he entered his oratory and knelt, summoning the bystanders, and said, "Let us give thanks to Our Lord, Who has thought us worthy to discover so many good things." He was extremely zealous for the divine service, eager and desirous for the conversion of these people [the Indians] and that in all parts the faith of Jesus Christ should be planted and enlarged. . . .

He was a gentleman of great spirit and vigor, of lofty thoughts, naturally inclined to undertake worthy deeds . . . patient and long-suffering . . . and a pardoner of injuries who sought nothing more . . . than that those who had offended him should recognize their errors. . . . He was very constant and endowed with forbearance in labors and adversities . . . always having great trust in divine providence. 　　　　　　　　　　　　(*Las Casas*)

MARCO POLO'S ASIA

The destination Columbus hoped to reach in his voyage had been described nearly two hundred years before by a medieval land traveler, Marco Polo. Marco Polo's *Book Concerning the Kingdoms and Marvels of the East* inspired the navigators of the fifteenth century to search for a sea route to the riches of Cathay. With that book's first mention of Cipangu [Japan] it became a trusted guide for Columbus, who wrote all over the margins of his copy.

Not since Alexander the Great found his way to India (327 B.C.) had so extensive a land exploration been recorded. In the space of twenty-four years, Marco Polo traveled thirty thousand miles. His *Book* is the chief geographical work of the Middle Ages.

In spite of his romantic accomplishments, Marco himself was not a daredevil adventurer but a sober Venetian merchant, interested in trade and money-making. He was fond of hunting, and was a keen but rather humorless observer. In 1271, at the age of fifteen, he had set out across Asia with his father Nicolo and uncle Maffeo for the court of the Grand Khan, not to gather material for a book but to make a fortune.

After arriving at the Mongol capital of Peking, Marco became a favorite of the ruler, Kublai Khan. He served on the Privy Council, governed a Chinese city for three years, and journeyed, protected by the Khan's "Tablet of Gold" from Peking to the China Sea. (The Tablet of Gold was a kind of credit card; the Grand Khan's subjects had to provide the bearer of the tablet with any goods he needed.) In 1295, after escorting a princess to Persia for her marriage there, the Polos returned to Venice.

"Marco Millions" the Venetians then called Marco Polo, either mocking at his claim to possess fabulous riches, or referring disparagingly to "Marco of the Thousand Stories." His *Book* was at first received with equal skepticism by the rest of Europe. Why, he described a great island—Cipangu —with palaces roofed with gold, lying fifteen hundred miles off the coast of China, whereas Ptolemy mentioned no such land! As for the "black stones" (coal) used in heating, and other marvels—these were simply laughed at.

On his deathbed, Marco was urged by well-meaning friends to retract his "lying" statements. Marco's solemn eyes, which had noted so many strange customs from burning Ormuz to Tibet, flashed.

"I have not told one half of what I have really seen!" he cried.

In the end, Marco's *Book* triumphed, just as Marco, his father, and uncle had when they returned to Venice. At first shut out of their own house, they were finally admitted, and made their fellow citizens gasp as they ripped precious jewels from the linings of their clothes.

The Polos could journey overland to Cathay because the Mongols had conquered Moslem kingdoms which once barred the way. For a hundred years the new guardians of the road kept it open to Christian missionaries, ambassadors, and merchants. But in the fourteenth century the Mongols were driven out of China, and the Moslem Turks barred the way in the Near East. The "Open Door" was closed, and now Marco Polo's *Book* became all the more valuable for the light it threw on the inaccessible East.

The selections below include the descriptions of Cathay and Cipangu which fascinated Columbus. Marco Polo wrote his *Book* in 1298, in French—with the help of a "ghost writer" named Rustician—while he was spending a year in a Genoese prison after having been captured in battle. It was soon translated into the other chief European languages, and was first printed in Germany in 1477.

Kinsay

The most noble city of Kinsay [Hangchow], a name which is as much as to say in our tongue "The City of Heaven" . . . is beyond dispute the finest and the noblest [city] in the world. . . .

First and foremost . . . Kinsay [is] so great that it hath an hundred miles of compass. And there are in it twelve thousand bridges of stone, for the most

part so lofty that a great fleet could pass beneath them . . . for . . . the whole city stands as it were in the water and surrounded by water. . . .

Inside the city there is a Lake which has a compass of some thirty miles: and all round it are erected beautiful palaces and mansions . . . belonging to the nobles of the city. There are also on its shores many abbeys and churches of the Idolaters. In the middle of the Lake are two Islands, on each of which stands a rich, beautiful and spacious edifice. . . . And when any one of the citizens desired to hold a marriage feast, or to give any other entertainment, it used to be done at one of these palaces. And everything would be found there ready to order, such as silver plate, trenchers, and dishes. . . .

The houses of the city are provided with lofty towers of stone in which articles of value are stored for fear of fire; for most of the houses themselves are of timber, and fires are very frequent in the city.

The people are Idolaters; and . . . they use paper money. Both men and women are fair and comely, and for the most part clothe themselves in silk. . . . [They] are men of peaceful character . . . [who] know nothing of handling arms and keep none in their houses. . . . Both in their commercial dealings and in their manufactures they are thoroughly honest and truthful. . . .

Since the Grand Khan occupied the city he has ordained that each of the twelve thousand bridges should be provided with a guard of ten men, in case

of any disturbance, or . . . treason. . . . Each guard
is provided with a hollow instrument of wood and
with a metal basin, and with a timekeeper to enable
him to know the hour of the day or night. And so
when one hour of the night is past the sentry strikes
one on the wooden instrument and on the basin. . . .
At the second hour he gives two strokes, and so
on. . . .

All the streets . . . are paved with stone or brick
. . . so that you ride and travel . . . without inconvenience. Were it not for this pavement you could
not do so, for the country is very low and flat, and
after rain 'tis deep in mire and water. . . .

Moreover . . . in this city there are . . . 1,600,000
houses. . . . It is the custom for every burgess . . .
to write over his door his own name, the name of
his wife, and those of his children, his slaves, and all
the inmates of his house. . . . In this way, the sover-
eign is able to know exactly the population of the
city. . . .

On the Lake of which we have spoken there are
numbers of boats and barges of all sizes for parties
of pleasure. These will hold ten, fifteen, twenty, or
more persons, and are from 15 to 20 paces in length,
with flat bottoms and ample breadth of beam. . . .
[They] are . . . completely furnished with tables and
chairs. . . . The roof forms a level deck, on which
the crew stand and pole the boat along . . . for the
Lake is not more than 2 paces in depth. The inside
of this roof and the rest of the interior is covered

with ornamental painting in gay colors, with windows all around . . . so that the party at table can enjoy all the beauty . . . of the prospects on both sides as they pass along.

Cipangu

Cipangu is an Island toward the east in the high seas, fifteen hundred miles distant from the Continent; and a very great Island it is.

The people are white, civilized, and well-favored. They are Idolaters, and are dependent on nobody. And . . . the quantity of gold they have is endless; for they find it in their own Islands, and the King does not allow it to be exported. Moreover few merchants visit the country because it is so far from the mainland, and thus . . . their gold is abundant beyond all measure. . . .

You must know that [the lord of that island] hath a great Palace which is entirely roofed with fine gold, just as our churches are roofed with lead. . . . Moreover, all the pavement of the Palace, and the floors of its chambers, are entirely of gold, in plates like slabs of stone, a good two fingers thick; and the windows also are of gold, so that altogether the richness of this Palace is past . . . all belief.

They have also pearls in abundance, which are of a rose color, but fine, big, and round, and quite as valuable as the white ones. In this Island some of the dead are buried, and others are burned. When a body is burned, they put one of these pearls in the mouth.

. . . They have also quantities of other precious stones.

The Spice Islands

The Sea in which lie the Islands [the Spice Islands of Indonesia] of those parts is called the Sea of Chin [the South China Sea]. . . . And . . . there be 7,459 Islands in . . . that Eastern Sea of Chin. . . .

And there is not one of those Islands but produces valuable and odorous woods like the lignaloe . . . and they produce also a great variety of spices. For example, in those Islands grows pepper as white as snow, as well as the black in great quantities. In fact the riches of those Islands is something wonderful, whether in gold or precious stones, or in all manner of spicery; but they lie so far off from the mainland that it is hard to get to them.

And when the ships of Zayton [Tsuen-chau or Chang-chau] and Kinsay [Hangchow] do voyage thither, they make vast profits. . . . It takes them a whole year . . . going in winter and returning in summer. For in that Sea there are but two winds that blow, the one that carries them outward and the other that brings them homeward; and the one of these winds blows all the winter [the northeast monsoon] and the other all the summer [the southwest monsoon]. And . . . these regions are . . . [also] far from India.

Marco Polo was the first to announce to Europe the existence of Japan, the first to describe the rich Spice Islands of Indonesia, the first to reveal the wealth and commerce of China—in his day the most civilized nation in the world. He used the name "Chin" [China] only in a maritime connection, however, as above. China was so called when reached by sea, but was known as Cathay when journeyed to overland. The Greeks and Romans called Cathay "Seres."

NOTES FOR A VOYAGE

In planning to reach Marco Polo's East by sailing west, Columbus had a problem to solve. For how long a voyage should he prepare? How far would he be sailing?

The clever Greek Eratosthenes, the founder of mathematical geography who had correctly estimated the circumference of the earth at 25,000 miles, would have warned him that he faced a trip of over 10,000 miles. On the other hand, the Florentine geographer Toscanelli said 5,000 miles.

To solve the problem, Columbus needed to know how many degrees of the earth's east-west circumference—that is, how many degrees of longitude—were covered by the *orbis terrarum* and how many miles one degree of longitude measured. For answers he turned to Ptolemy, Pierre d'Ailly, Marco Polo, and the Arab Alfragan.

Ptolemy taught that the land from the Canaries to China covered half the surface of the earth (180°); by that reckoning he made his China extend 1,600 miles east of where Japan really lies. But the fifteenth century Pierre d'Ailly, Columbus's favorite geographer, pushed the Chinese coast so far east that it overlapped Alaska (225° covered by land). When Columbus added 28° for Marco Polo's province of Cathay and 30° for Marco Polo's Cipangu, he brought Cipangu, that is, Japan, out into the Atlantic

Ocean east of Cuba! This reduced the Ocean Sea west of the Canaries to a pond covering only 68° of the earth's surface. Thinking that he detected a mistake in one of his authorities, Columbus promptly changed that figure to 60°.

He then adopted the smallest figure for the miles covered by 1° of longitude, that of the Arab geographer Alfragan, or at least as he understood Alfragan: 45 nautical miles at the equator. In the latitude of the Canaries, this was reduced to 40, so Columbus planned to sail 60 × 40, or 2,400, nautical miles (about 2,760 statute miles) west and dock in Japan! Since the correct airline distance from the Canaries to Japan is 10,600 miles (about 12,200 statute miles), we must agree with the Portuguese mathematicians who for reasons of their own awarded Columbus an "F" for his solution of the problem when he appeared before them.

The geography notes below reveal Columbus's ideas about the size of the globe and the eastward trend of the *orbis terrarum*. Columbus jotted them in the margins of Pierre d'Ailly's *Imago Mundi* ("Concerning the Form of the World," written 1410, printed 1480).

Aristotle [says that] between the end of Spain and the beginning of India is a small sea, navigable in a few days.

Esdras [says that] six parts of the earth are habitable and the seventh is covered with water.

From the end of the West all the way to the end of India by land is much more than half [the circumference of] the earth, viz. 180°; the eastern side [of the earth] is near Africa or Spain.

The end of the habitable earth in the East and the end of the habitable earth in the West are near, and between is a small sea.

Each degree has 56 2/3 [Roman] miles.

Water runs from pole to pole in the sea, and extends between the end of Spain and the beginning of India; [this sea is] not very wide.

India is near Spain.

From the end of the West, namely Portugal, all the way to the end of the East, namely India, by land is a great distance.

The amount of land is much greater than the multitude of philosophers thinks.

THE ROUTE TO CIPANGU

Fifteenth century geographers could not agree on the size of the *orbis terrarum*, or Island of Earth. Some argued that it was comparatively small—that there was a great expanse of water between Spain and Asia. But others cited the apocryphal Book of Esdras as Columbus did (six-sevenths of the globe habitable), and extended the *orbis terrarum* far to the east and south. More land meant less water, a narrow Ocean Sea which made Columbus's westward voyage seem feasible.

Paolo Toscanelli, a Florentine physician whose hobby was geography, was a "wide Asia" man who encouraged Columbus. In 1474, in a letter to a Portuguese churchman, Canon Martins, Toscanelli had urged the Portuguese to reach the East by sailing west. When Columbus wrote Toscanelli, the physician sent him a copy of the letter to Martins, along with a "sea chart" which showed the route to Cipangu by way of "the island of Antillia." When Columbus wrote a second time, Toscanelli sent him a shorter letter of approval.

Passages from Toscanelli's letters are printed below, but the "sea chart," which Columbus may have taken with him in 1492, has been lost. On his voyages to the West Indies Columbus was constantly looking for the "powerful kingdoms and noble cities and rich provinces, abounding in . . . spices and jewels," which Toscanelli had assured him he would find.

Paolo the physician, to Christopher Columbus, Greetings.

I perceive your noble and grand desire to go to the places where the spices grow; and in reply to your letter I send you a copy of another letter which some time since I sent to a . . . gentleman of the household of the most serene King of Portugal . . . and I send you another sea chart like the one I sent him. . . .

Paolo the physician, to Fernão Martins, canon of Lisbon, Greetings.

. . . I have often before spoken of a sea route from

here to the Indies, where the spices grow, a route shorter than the one which you are pursuing by way of Guinea. You tell me that His Highness desires from me some . . . demonstration that would make it easier to understand and take that route. I could do this by using a sphere . . . but I decided that it would be easier . . . if I showed that route by means of a sea chart.

I therefore send His Majesty a chart drawn by my own hand, upon which is laid out the western coast from Ireland on the north to the end of Guinea, and the islands which lie on that route, in front of which, directly to the west, is shown the beginning of the Indies, with the islands and places at which you are bound to arrive, and how far from the Arctic Pole or the Equator you ought to keep away, and . . . how many leagues intervene before you reach those places most fertile in all sorts of spices, jewels, and precious stones. . . .

From the city of Lisbon due west there are twenty-six spaces marked on the map, each of which contains two hundred and fifty miles, as far as the very great and noble city of Kinsay [Hangchow]. . . . And from the island of Antillia, which you call the Island of the Seven Cities, to the very noble island of Cipangu, there are ten spaces, which make 2,500 miles. . . . This land is most rich in gold, pearls, and precious stones, and the temples and royal palaces are covered with solid gold. . . .

I remain ready to serve His Highness and answer

his questions at greater length if he should order me to do so.

Done in the city of Florence, June 15, 1474.

Paolo the physician, to Christopher Columbus, Greetings.

I have received your letters together with the things you sent me, and took great pleasure in them. I perceive your grand and noble desire to sail from west to east by the route indicated on the map I sent you. . . . I am much pleased to see that I have been well understood, and that the voyage has become not only possible but certain, fraught with inestimable honor and gain. . . .

When that voyage shall be made, it will be a voyage to powerful kingdoms and noble cities and rich provinces, abounding in . . . all manner of spices and jewels. . . . It will also be a voyage to kings and princes who are very eager to have friendly dealings and speech with the Christians of our countries, because many of them are Christians; they are also very eager to know and speak with the learned men of our lands concerning religion and all other branches of knowledge, because of the much they have heard of the empires and governments of these parts.

For these reasons . . . I do not wonder that you, who are of great courage . . . are now inflamed with desire to undertake this voyage.

DRIFTWOOD AND PHANTOM ISLANDS

Flung out into the eastern Atlantic like shining pebbles lie the green Azores and the Madeiras. These outposts of Europe provided Columbus with further evidence that he could reach land by sailing west.

Visiting them, he heard rumors of curious driftwood and of mysterious islands farther west that seemed to point to Cathay. Toscanelli had placed Antillia only 2,500 miles from Cipangu—why should there not be other as yet undiscovered islands which could serve as way stations on his voyage? When Columbus saw a rock which seemed to be a statue of a horseman pointing west, on Corvo in the Azores, he eagerly took that as an omen for his "Enterprise."

Actually, the driftwood reported in these archipelagoes was a trustworthy clue. Westerly winds do carry light objects from the Caribbean to the Azores. Bluish, black-striped trunks of the Central American cuipo tree were washed there in the nineteenth century, and horse beans—seeds of a Caribbean climber—are found on the beaches today after a storm. But the "two dead bodies with broad faces" which Columbus took for Chinese were probably Finns or Lapps—and the western islands were imaginary.

The following selection from Ferdinand Columbus's *The Life of the Admiral Christopher Columbus* (1571) lists these signs of land to the west.

The Admiral's [Columbus's] third and last motive for seeking the Indies was his hope of finding before he arrived there some island or land of great importance. . . . He found support for this hope in the authority of many learned men . . . who were certain that the land area of the globe was greater than that of the water. This being so, he argued that between the end of Spain and the known end of India there must be many other islands and lands. . . .

He believed this all the more because . . . [of] the many . . . stories which he heard from various persons and sailors who traded to the western islands and . . . the Azores and Madeira. Since these stories served his design, he was careful to file them away in his memory. . . .

A pilot of the Portuguese King, Martin Vincente by name, told him [Columbus] that . . . four hundred and fifty leagues west of Cape St. Vincent, he fished out of the sea a piece of wood ingeniously carved, but not with iron. For this reason and because for many days the winds had blown from the west, he concluded this wood came from some islands to the west.

Pedro Correa, who was married to a sister of the Admiral's wife, told him that on the island of Porto Santo he had seen another piece of wood brought by the same wind, carved as well as the aforementioned one, and that canes had also drifted in, so thick that one joint held nine decanters of wine. . . . Since such canes do not grow anywhere in our lands, he was sure that the wind had blown them from some neighboring islands or perhaps from India. Ptolemy . . . writes that such canes are found in the eastern parts of the Indies.

Some persons in the Azores also told him that after

the wind had blown for a long time from the west, the sea cast on the shores of those islands . . . pine trees that do not grow . . . anywhere in that region. On . . . Flores, which is one of the Azores, the sea flung ashore two dead bodies with broad faces and different in appearance from the Christians. . . .

In addition to these signs . . . some claimed to have seen certain islands. . . . The Admiral . . . tells that in 1484 an inhabitant of the island of Madeira came to Portugal to ask the King for a caravel in order to discover some land which he swore he saw every year and always in the same situation. . . .

One Diogo de Teive . . . went in search of . . . [Antillia]. . . . On their return they discovered the island of Flores [one of the Azores], to which they were guided by the many birds they saw flying in that direction; as they knew them to be land and not marine birds, they decided they must be flying to some resting place. . . .

A one-eyed sailor in the port of Santa Maria [one of the Azores] . . . told [Columbus] that on a voyage he had made to Ireland he saw . . . land, which at the time he supposed to be a part of Tartary; that it turned westward . . . and that foul weather prevented them from approaching it.

THREE EQUIPPED CARAVELS

After Queen Isabella accepted Columbus's "Enterprise of the Indies," officials drew up a contract, a grant of titles and offices to Columbus and his heirs, a letter addressed to Eastern rulers (such as the Grand Khan), a passport, and several royal decrees, the most important of which ordered the town of Palos to provide him with two caravels. These documents were made out April 17 and April 30, 1492.

By the terms of the contract and grant of titles, Columbus was to have the titles of Admiral of the Ocean Sea and of Viceroy of all islands and mainlands he discovered— and his descendants would inherit both these offices. He would also receive one-tenth of all "pearls, precious stones, gold, silver, spices, and other objects" he found, and would have the privilege of contributing one-eighth of the expenses of any future expedition in return for one-eighth of the profits.

These were the same terms King John II of Portugal had considered too high when he dismissed Columbus.

Columbus's contract (Articles of Agreement) and letter to Eastern rulers (Letter of Credence) are printed below.

Articles of Agreement

The things prayed for, and which Your Highnesses give and grant to Don Christopher Columbus as some recompense for . . . the voyage which now, with the help of God, he has engaged to make . . . in the service of Your Highnesses, are the following:

Firstly, that Your Highnesses, as actual Lords of the . . . Oceans, appoint from this date the said Don Christopher Columbus to be your Admiral in all those islands and mainlands which by his activity and industry shall be discovered or acquired in the said oceans, during his lifetime, and likewise, after his death, his heirs and successors . . . in perpetuity. . . .

Likewise, that Your Highnesses appoint the said Don Christopher Columbus to be your Viceroy and Governor General in all the said islands and mainlands . . . which . . . he may discover . . . ; and that for the government of each . . . of them he may make choice of three persons for each office, and that Your Highnesses may . . . choose the one who shall be most serviceable to you. . . .

Item, that of all and every kind of merchandise, whether pearls, precious stones, gold, silver, spices, and other objects . . . which may be bought, bartered, discovered, acquired and obtained within the limits of the said Admiralty, Your Highnesses grant . . . that he may . . . take for himself, the tenth part of the whole, after deducting all the expenses which may be incurred therein. . . .

Likewise, that if on account of the merchandise which he might bring from the said islands and lands . . . or of that which may be taken in exchange for the same . . . any suit should arise . . . he or his deputy . . . shall . . . give judgment in the same. . . .

Item, that in all the vessels which may be equipped for the said traffic . . . whenever . . . they may be equipped, the said Don Christopher Columbus may, if he chooses, contribute and pay the eighth part of all that may be spent in the equipment, and . . . may have . . . the eighth part of the profits. . . .

These are granted and dispatched . . . in the town

of Santa Fe de la Vega of Granada, on the 17th day of April, A.D. 1492.

I THE KING   I THE QUEEN

Letter of Credence

To the most serene prince _____, our most dear friend, Ferdinand and Isabella, King and Queen of Castile, Aragon, León, Sicily, etc., greetings and increase of good fortune. From the reports of certain subjects of Ours, and of others who have come to Us from those kingdoms and districts [of yours], we have joyfully understood how you are well disposed and feel good will toward Us and Our state, and with what great eagerness you wish to be informed of Our prosperous affairs. Wherefore we have determined to send to you Our noble captain Christopher Columbus, the bearer of these, from whom you will be able to learn about Our good health and prosperous condition, and other matters which We have commanded him to report to you on Our part. And so We ask you to have absolute faith in his reports, as you would in Us, which will be most pleasing to Us, who hold ourselves ready and disposed to please You. From Our city of Granada. 30 April, A.D. 1492.

I THE KING   I THE QUEEN

On May 23, 1492, Columbus stood proudly in the Church of St. George, in Palos, while the town notary read aloud the royal decree ordering Palos to "have all ready and prepared two equipped caravels . . . within ten days." But he might have had to wait months for both ships and crews had it not been for the Pinzóns.

Martín Alonso Pinzón, a bluff, veteran mariner and the leading citizen of Palos, put himself and his family behind Columbus's project. (He believed a story that the Old Testament Queen of Sheba had once voyaged west to Cipangu.) Before Martín Alonso spoke up, seamen "thought that the enterprise was vain," muttering that the Portuguese "had gone to discover" in the Western Ocean and found nothing.

Now word went around that Martín Alonso was to captain one of the two caravels, the *Pinta;* his younger brother Vincente would captain the *Niña,* with another Pinzón as master of the *Pinta* and still another—known as "the old boy"—a common seaman on the same vessel. So the adventurous young men of this district of Aragon began to enlist—and it was said they were so versed in the sea that the fishes of the Mediterranean wore the red and gold bars of Aragon on their silver coats.

A retired seaman who had sailed with the Portuguese de Teive in 1452 when the crew thought they were near land west of Ireland "encouraged the people and told them . . . that all should go on that voyage and they would find a very rich land." This ancient mariner told Columbus and Martín Alonso Pinzón "that he had information of the land of the Indies."

A crew of ninety enrolled, of whom seventy-one came from around Palos or from other towns in southern Spain, and only four were not Spaniards (three Italians and a Portuguese). In addition, there were several "specialists": an interpreter, Luís de Torres, whose Hebrew and Arabic were supposed to enable him to converse with the Grand Khan; a marshal to maintain discipline; a secretary to write up proceedings when Columbus took possession of new lands; and a comptroller to keep an eye on the Crown's funds.

Columbus himself chartered the third ship, the *nao Santa María* from Galicia. Provisions for a year were taken, along with cheap trading goods—red caps, glass beads, brass rings, "hawk's bells"—such as the Portuguese had found suitable for primitive West Africans. On August 2—the day on which the Jews, who had traveled weeping and lamenting to the coasts, their carts laden with household wares, were expelled from Spain—Columbus completed his preparations. He filled his water casks at a fountain near the Church of St. George, and he and his men went to Confession and Communion. He whom the courtiers mocked as a "dreamer" had waited eight years for this moment.

On Friday, August 3, 1492, writes the historian Oviedo, Christopher Columbus "with three equipped caravels . . . entered upon the sea . . . in the name of Jesus, ordered the sails to be set, and left the port of Palos for . . . the Ocean Sea."

Chapter Four

◦───◦

INTO THE UNKNOWN

*Your Highnesses . . . ordained that I should not go
[to India] by land to the eastward . . . but by way
of the west.*

　　　　　　　—CHRISTOPHER COLUMBUS, *Journal*

Columbus decided to keep a diary for the *Santa María*—a journal of his voyage. He had never doubted the importance of what he was attempting, nor that he would succeed. Now he would put the events in writing so that the whole world—especially Ferdinand and Isabella—could know what he had accomplished!

He used rough, simple seaman's language, often repeating himself. He made mistakes in his Spanish, but he was to describe the winds, waves, fish, and seaweed of the uncharted Atlantic, the plants, animals, and peoples he found in the "Indies," so vividly that his *Journal* has become a classic of geography. Nor would he neglect to give the sovereigns hints about the empire they might develop, so they would finance another, more elaborate expedition. Above all, he would tell the story of his discovery.

Facts were taken from Columbus's *Journal* by Ferdinand Columbus for his *Historie (Life of the Admiral Christopher Columbus)* and by Las Casas for his *Historia de las Indias (History of the Indies)*, but the *Journal* was apparently unknown to other early historians. It was not printed until 1825, after the manuscript was discovered by the scholar Navarette in the library of a Spanish duke.

The manuscript found by Navarrete was not Columbus's original *Journal*, which had been lost, but a *summary* of that original made by Las Casas. Las Casas copied Columbus's own words, merely omitting repetitions and unimportant details, but he used the third person form "the admiral" and "he" instead of Columbus's "I." When he quoted Columbus word for word, the passage is placed in quotation marks and often identified as being "the words of the admiral."

For the next four chapters, we will be reading Las Casas'

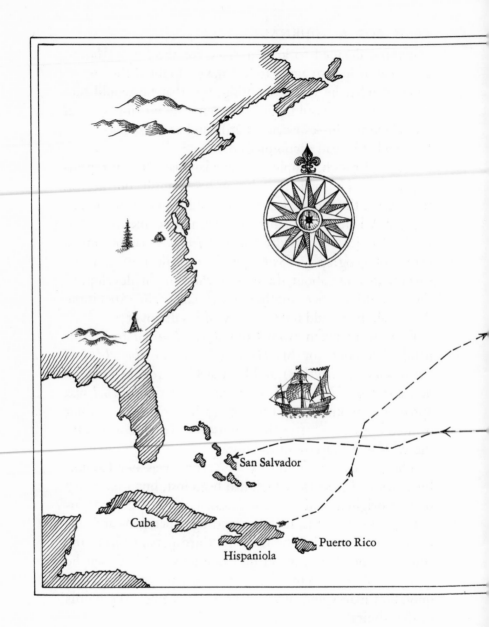

San Salvador

Cuba

Hispaniola

Puerto Rico

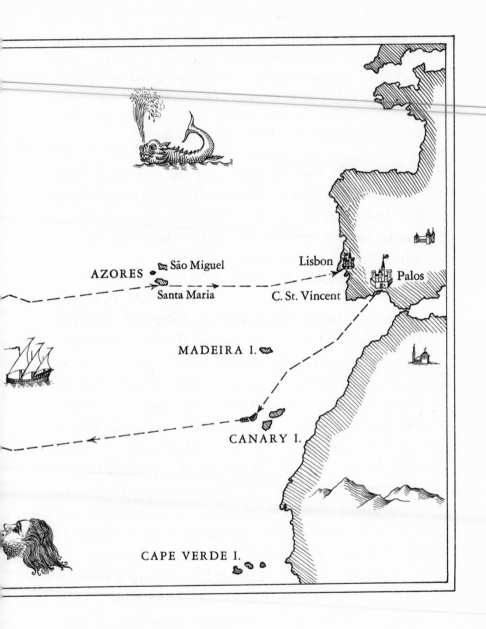

AZORES   São Miguel   Lisbon

Santa Maria   C. St. Vincent   Palos

MADEIRA I.

CANARY I.

CAPE VERDE I.

summary of Columbus's *Journal* (English translation by
Cecil Jane). Unless otherwise indicated, all selections in
these four chapters are from the *Journal*, whose Spanish
title is *El Libro de la Primera Navegación* ("Book of the
First Navigation"). The passage below is from the Prologue addressed to Ferdinand and Isabella.

This is the First Voyage, and the courses and the
way, that the Admiral Don Christopher Columbus
pursued when he discovered the Indies, set forth in
the form of a summary, save for the Prologue . . .
which begins in this manner:
"IN THE NAME OF OUR LORD JESUS CHRIST.
"Most Christian and most exalted and most excellent and most mighty princes, King and Queen of
the Spains and of the islands of the sea, our Sovereigns: Forasmuch as, in this present year of 1492
. . . in . . . January . . . on the ground of information
which I had given to Your Highnesses concerning
the lands of India, and concerning a prince who is
called 'Grand Khan' . . . Your Highnesses . . . took
thought to send me, Christopher Columbus, to . . .
India, to see those princes and peoples and . . . to
bring about their conversion to our holy faith, and
ordained that I should not go by land to the eastward . . . but by way of the west . . . therefore . . .
Your Highnesses . . . accorded to me great rewards
and ennobled me so that . . . I might style myself
'don' and be high admiral of the Ocean Sea and viceroy and perpetual governor of the islands and con-

tinent which I should discover . . . and that my eldest son should succeed to the same position, and so on from generation to generation.

"And I departed from . . . Granada . . . [in] May . . . 1492 . . . and came to the town of Palos . . . where I made ready three ships . . . and I set out from that port, well furnished with very many supplies and with many seamen, on the third day of . . . August of the same year, on a Friday, half an hour before the rising of the sun, and I steered my course for the Canary Islands . . . thence . . . to sail until I should arrive in the Indies, and deliver the embassy of Your Highnesses to those princes and perform all that you had commanded me to do.

"To this end, I thought to write all this journey very carefully, from day to day, all that I might do and see and experience. . . . In addition to writing each night that which the day had brought forth and each day how I had sailed at night, I design to make a new chart for navigation, in which I will set all the sea and lands of the Ocean Sea in their true places, under their bearings . . . by latitude from the equinoctial line [the equator] and by longitude from the west. . . . And these things will be a great labor."

On the outward voyage, Columbus computed each day from sunrise of the day named to sunrise of the next day; on the homeward voyage, from sunset to sunset. He did not make the "chart for navigation," probably because he found he could not determine latitude and longitude accurately.

RUDDER TROUBLE

An ebb tide carried Columbus's three ships down the Rio Tinto from Palos and into the Atlantic. There a sea breeze filled the white sails painted with great red crosses, and the fleet headed south by west for the Canary Islands.

Columbus had several reasons for taking this route to Cipangu. First, he knew that the Portuguese had always been beaten back by opposing winds when they tried to sail west in the latitude of the Azores and Spain. Second, he had discovered that the northeast trade wind blew farther south, through the Canaries (sixty miles west of Africa), and counted on this wind to give him a good start. Finally, Martin Behaim's globe and other maps mistakenly showed Cipangu on the same parallel of latitude as the Canaries, and it was the practice of navigators to go first to the latitude of their destination, then follow that parallel to port.

The seven Canary Islands extend east to west to form a flat saucer. Sailing into this mountainous group from the north, Columbus sent the crippled *Pinta* to Grand Canary Island while he continued farther west to Gomera Island to look for a ship with which to replace it. On the way he passed 12,200-foot Tenerife Island, with its volcanic peak emerging like a diamond from the dense sea-cloud around its base. But he could find no ship to lease and returned to Grand Canary, where the *Pinta* was repaired and *Niña*'s triangular lateen sails, which had proved awkward in a following wind, were changed to square sails. Some crew members began to complain of "difficulties" and "toil," but there were no desertions.

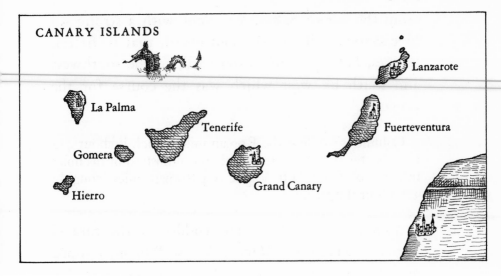

On a second visit to Gomera, Columbus—according to tradition—met and fell in love with the beautiful young widow who ruled that island, Doña Beatriz de Peraza. However, he remained faithful to his Enterprise of the Indies and departed promptly at dawn, September 6. Three days later the last land dropped astern below the horizon.

"Many sighed and wept for fear they would not see it again for a long time," says Ferdinand Columbus. But "the Admiral comforted them with great promises of lands and riches."

The following selection describes the "shakedown" cruise to the Canaries and the stopover there.

"Friday, August 3 On Friday, the third day of August, of the year 1492, at eight o'clock, we set out

from the bar of Saltés. We went with a strong sea breeze sixty miles to the southward, that is, fifteen leagues, before sunset; afterward, to the southwest and south by west which was the course for the Canaries."

Columbus's mile is the Roman mile, which is about 424 feet shorter than ours. It would take almost 10 of his miles to make 9 of ours. His league is 4 Roman miles—roughly 3.7 of our statute miles.

Monday, August 6   The rudder of the caravel *Pinta,* in which was Martín Alonso Pinzón, jumped out of gear; this was believed or suspected to be due to the action of a certain Gomez Rascón and Cristóbal Quintero, to whom the caravel belonged, because that voyage was irksome to him [Quintero]. . . . Before they set out, these men had been . . . inclined to oppose and pick holes [find fault], as they say.

The admiral was then much disturbed because he could not help the caravel without danger to himself, and he says that his anxiety was somewhat relieved because he knew that Martín Alonso Pinzón was a man of courage and of good understanding. Eventually, day and night together, they went twenty-nine leagues.

Tuesday, August 7   The rudder of the *Pinta* again was unshipped and they repaired it, and they went on a course for the island of Lanzarote, which

is one of the Canary Islands. And they made twenty-
five leagues, day and night together.

Wednesday, August 8   Among the pilots of the
three caravels there were different opinions concerning their position, and the admiral proved to be
nearest the truth. He was anxious to go to Grand
Canary, in order to leave the caravel *Pinta* there,
since she was steering badly and making water, and
he wished to secure another there, if one were to be
found. They were not able to arrive there on that day.

*Thursday, August 9 [to Wednesday, September
5]*   Until the night of Sunday, the admiral could
not make Gomera, and Martín Alonso, by order of
the admiral, remained off that coast of Grand Canary,
because he could not steer. Afterward the admiral
reached [Grand] Canary . . . and with much labor
and care on the part of the admiral, of Martín
Alonso, and of the others they repaired the *Pinta*
very well, and eventually they reached Gomera.

They saw a great fire coming from the mountain
of the island of Tenerife, which is remarkably lofty.
They fitted the *Niña* with square sails, for she had
been lateen rigged. He [Columbus] returned to
Gomera on Sunday, the second of September, with
the *Pinta* repaired.

The admiral says that many honorable Spaniards
. . . who were in Gomera . . . swore that every year
they saw land [St. Brendan's Island] to the westward of the Canaries, which is toward the setting

sun. . . . The admiral here says that he remembers that, being in Portugal in the year 1484, one from the island of Madeira came to the king and asked of him a caravel, to go to this land which he saw, and that this man swore that he saw it every year. . . . He also remembers that they said the same thing in the islands of the Azores. . . .

Having taken in water and wood and meat . . . finally he [Columbus] set sail from the island of Gomera, with his three caravels, on Thursday, the sixth day of September.

Thursday, September 6   He set out on that day in the morning from the harbor of Gomera. . . . And the admiral learned from a caravel, which came from the island of Hierro, that three caravels of Portugal were cruising there, in order to take him. This must have been due to the envy which the king [of Portugal] felt because he [Columbus] had gone to Castile. And he went all that day and night in a calm, and in the morning he found himself between Gomera and Tenerife.

The Portuguese caravels had perhaps come to see that Columbus's fleet did not sail south into the waters off the Guinea coast, which the Portuguese considered exclusively theirs. Columbus did not sight the Portuguese ships.

Friday, September 7   All Friday and Saturday, until three o'clock at night, he was becalmed.

Saturday, September 8   At three o'clock at night,

on the Saturday, it began to blow from the northeast, and he shaped his route and course to the west. He shipped much sea over the bows, which made progress slow, and that day and night he went nine leagues.

Sunday, September 9 He made fifteen leagues that day, and he determined to reckon less than he made, in order that the crews might thus not become disheartened or alarmed if the voyage were lengthy. In the night he went 120 miles, at ten miles an hour, which is thirty leagues. The sailors steered badly, letting her fall off to west by north and even to west-northwest; concerning this the admiral many times rebuked them.

Columbus's famous false reckoning—designed, as he says, to help the men's morale—was actually more accurate than his secret "true" reckoning. He overestimated his speed and distance in the "true" reckoning by about the same amount (9 per cent) that he underestimated it for the crews.

A SEA OF GRASS

For the first ten days beyond the Canaries the northeast trade wind blew steadily, and the three ships scudded west under clear skies. Columbus was confident that after a "few days," as his geography books promised, he would reach Cipangu. The month's voyage he anticipated would be shorter than the trip by sea from Italy to Britain or from Normandy to Palestine.

His only problem was a psychological one: On this journey into the unknown, how long would the crews' nerves hold out? Even during calms, when they could swim, fish, or loll on deck, there were subdued murmurs because they feared they would never return.

When the compass needle apparently veered from true north, even though Columbus explained correctly that it was not the needle that moved but the Pole Star itself (describing a radius of 3° 27′ around the celestial pole in 1492), they were frightened. When a "marvelous branch of fire" (a meteor) streaked through the sky, they groaned, "It is a sign—we have not undertaken a good journey!"

On September 16, nine hundred miles out, they sighted what looked like a great green and yellow meadow stretching from horizon to horizon—the Sargasso Sea. Then the sailors did indeed stare at each other in alarm. According to legend, this "meadow" was the graveyard of ships. Vessels would get stuck in it, as St. Amador had been icebound, and drift together in one rotting mass in the center.

Columbus remembered what the retired seaman of Palos who had once sailed here had told him: there was no danger. The admiral gave the bold command, *"Adelante!"* ("Forward!"), and while the ships' lookouts strained to catch sight of sunken reefs or "drowned lands," the weed parted readily before the prows. At first the helmsmen sought patches of blue water in the maze, but soon sailed their ships straight through.

In actuality the Sargasso Sea, which Columbus was the first to describe factually, offers no hindrance to navigation. The weed is at most half an inch thick. The Sargasso, named for the Portuguese word for gulfweed (*sargaço*), spreads like a threadbare oval carpet on the Atlantic from

32° west longitude to the Bahamas, and from 40° north latitude to 18° north latitude—2,300 miles east to west, 1,500 north to south.

Columbus thought the weed grew on ledges near the Azores, from which it was torn loose and floated west, but in the twentieth century it was discovered that the algae reproduces itself. It is kept afloat by tiny globules (like blueberries) filled with air, which Columbus called the "fruit" of the gulfweed.

The following selection describes the first 1,339 miles of the voyage, beyond the Canary Islands.

Tuesday, September 11   That day they sailed on their course, which was to the west, and they made twenty leagues and more. And they saw a large piece of the mast of a ship of 120 tons, and they could not secure it. During the night they went about twenty leagues, and he [Columbus] reckoned no more than sixteen, for the said reason.

Thursday, September 13   In that day and night, following their course which was west, they went thirty-three leagues, and he reckoned three or four less. The currents were against them. On this day, at the beginning of the night, the needles turned northwest, and in the morning they declined northeast somewhat.

Friday, September 14   That day they navigated on their course westward, and during the night, and they went twenty leagues. He reckoned somewhat less. Here those in the caravel *Niña* said that they had seen a tern and a tropic bird; and these birds never go more than twenty-five leagues from land.

Saturday, September 15   He sailed that day with its night twenty-seven leagues and somewhat more on his westerly course. And on this night, at the beginning of it, they saw fall from the sky a marvelous branch of fire [a meteor] into the sea at a distance of four or five leagues from them.

Sunday, September 16   He went on his westerly course that day and night. They must have made thirty-nine leagues, but he did not reckon more than thirty-six. That day there were some clouds, a little rain falling. Here the admiral says that then and always after that time they met with very temperate breezes, so that it was a great delight to enjoy the mornings, and nothing was lacking except to hear nightingales. He says: "And the weather was like April in Andalusia [southern Spain]."

Here they began to see many tufts of very green seaweed, which, as it appeared, had not long been torn from the earth; on this account, all judged that they were near some island, but not to the mainland, according to the admiral, who says: "For the mainland I take to be further on."

Monday, September 17   He sailed on his westerly course, and they went in the day and night fifty leagues and more: he only counted forty-seven. The current assisted them. They saw much vegetation and it was very delicate and was weed from rocks; and the vegetation came from the westward. They concluded that they were near land.

The pilots took the north, marking it, and they found that the needles declined northwest a full point; and the sailors were alarmed and depressed, and they did not say why. When the admiral noticed this, he gave orders that they should mark the north again at dawn, and they found that the needles were true. The explanation was that the star appears to change its position and not the needles.

In the morning, on that Monday, they saw much more weed, and it seemed to be grass from rivers, and in this they found a live crab, which the admiral kept. And he says that these were certain signs of land, because they are not found eighty leagues from land. They found that the water of the sea was less salt, after they had left the Canaries, and the breezes constantly softer. They all went on their way greatly rejoicing. . . .

Tuesday, September 18 He navigated that day and night and they made more than fifty-five leagues, but he did not reckon more than forty-eight. All these days the sea was very smooth, like the river at Seville. On this day Martín Alonso in the *Pinta*, which was a fast sailer, did not wait; for he called to the admiral from his caravel that he had seen a great crowd of birds go toward the west, and hoped to sight land that night, and for this reason he so went ahead. To the northward there appeared a great bank of dark clouds, which is a sign of being near land.

SIGNS OF LAND

Columbus had begun to see "signs of land" on the fifth day after he lost sight of the Canaries. Now tiny crabs, thumbnail size among the gulfweed, sea fowl—the great white booby with black wing tips, the small Arctic tern—which Columbus mistook for land birds, a tuna fish, a whale—all were reckoned sure indications that at least the fleet was passing "through the midst of" islands.

Columbus optimistically tried the sounding lead, but found no bottom at 200 fathoms. (The Atlantic here is 2,292 fathoms deep and the nearest land is the Azores, 979 miles to the northeast.)

On September 19 the fleet passed out of the belt of trade winds for a few days. The sea gradually flattened; there was a stationary cloud bank, a drizzle of rain, a calm. The men had little to do but wish they were safe back in Spain. This ocean of prevailing northeast winds, few waves, and balmy air was "another world," they muttered. No west wind would ever stir up a high sea and blow them home!

The chart which Columbus and Martín Alonso Pinzón discussed on September 25 may have been the one Toscanelli had sent Columbus as a "road map" to the East. The land Pinzón sought that day was the imaginary island of Antillia, shown on the chart. The "high sea" which pleased Columbus was probably caused by a hurricane far to the southwest.

The following selection describes the growing uneasiness of the men and the first false landfall.

Wednesday, September 19   He sailed on his course, and in the day and night went twenty-five leagues, since it was calm. He wrote down twenty-two. This day, at ten o'clock, there came to the ship a booby [gannet], and in the evening they saw another, and it is not their habit to go farther than twenty leagues from land. A few drops of rain fell without wind; this is a certain indication of land.

The admiral did not wish to be delayed by beating to windward in order to make sure whether there was land in that direction, but he was certain that to the north and to the south there were some islands. . . . He went through the midst of them, because his wish was to press onward toward the Indies. . . .

Thursday, September 20   On this day he navigated west by north and west-northwest because, with the calm which prevailed, the winds were very variable. They must have made some seven or eight leagues. Two boobies came to the ship, and afterward another, which was a sign that they were near land, and they saw much vegetation, although on the previous day they had seen none. . . .

Friday, September 21   Most of that day it was calm, and afterward there was some wind. They must have gone, day and night together . . . some thirteen leagues. At dawn they found so much weed that the sea appeared to be choked with it, and it came from the west. . . . They saw a whale, which is a sign that they were near land, since they always remain near it.

Saturday, September 22   He navigated west-northwest, more or less, inclining to one side and to the other. They must have made thirty leagues; they saw hardly any vegetation. They saw some petrels and another bird. Here the admiral says: "This head wind was very necessary to me, since my people were much excited, because they thought that in these seas no winds ever blew to carry them back to Spain." For some part of the day there was no seaweed, afterward it was very dense.

Sunday, September 23   He sailed north-west-ward and at times northwest by north and at other times keeping to his course, which was to the west. . . . They saw a pigeon and a booby, and another river bird, and other white birds; there was much vegetation and in it they found crabs.

As the sea was calm and smooth, the people murmured, saying that as there was there no great sea, it would never blow so as to carry them back to Spain. But afterward the sea, without wind, rose greatly, and this amazed them, for which reason the admiral here says: "So that high sea was very necessary for me, because such a thing had not been seen save in the time of the Jews, when [those] of Egypt came out against Moses who was leading them out of captivity."

Tuesday, September 25 This day was very calm and afterward it blew, and they went on their way to the west until night. The admiral talked with Martín Alonso Pinzón, captain of . . . the *Pinta,* concerning a chart which three days before he had sent to him . . . and in which . . . the admiral had certain islands depicted as being in that sea. And Martín Alonso said that they were in that neighborhood, and the admiral replied that such was his opinion. . . .

At sunset Martín Alonso mounted the poop of his ship and in great delight called the admiral, asking for a reward from him because he had sighted land. The admiral says that, hearing this stated positively, he fell on his knees to give thanks to Our Lord, and Martín Alonso with his men said the *Gloria in excelsis Deo* ["Glory to God in the highest"].

The admiral's people did the same, and those in the *Niña* all climbed the mast and into the rigging, and all affirmed that it was land. And the admiral thought the same and that it was at twenty-five leagues distance. Until night they all continued to declare that it was land. . . .

The sea was very smooth, so that many sailors went swimming. They saw many dorados [dolphins] and other fish.

Wednesday, September 26 He sailed on his course to the west until after midday; then they went to the southwest, until it was found that what they had said was land was not land, but only cloud.

They made in the day and night thirty-one leagues, and he reckoned twenty-four to his men. The sea was like a river; the breezes sweet and very soft.

MUTINY

The conflict between Columbus and his crew was not one between a hero and ninety cowards, but one between a man with complete faith in his idea and others who had much less confidence in it. From the point of view of the seamen, there were sound reasons for turning back.

They had sailed over twice as far as any had ever gone before out of sight of land. All signs had failed, landfalls proved false, the ships leaked and might reach a condition in which repairs could not be made at sea. Also the crew knew that great scholars at the Spanish court were skeptical of Columbus's Enterprise, and that the voyage was even longer than publicly admitted—for the worried pilots had revealed Columbus's false reckoning of distances to the sailors.

During the first week of October, as the ships rushed westward, now back in the belt of the trade winds, members of the crew met in the dark holds. Insulting and violent words were spoken, often in Columbus's hearing:

"He is trying to make himself a lord at the cost of our lives!"

"We have already gone farther from land than any others. Why sail on to our ruin?"

"We are running out of food and the ships leak!"

"Let's quit talking and heave him overboard—we will say he fell while watching the stars!"

The evening of October 7 was remarkable for the great numbers of birds passing overhead, flying west-southwest. Columbus stared up, and then changed his course to follow them. By October 10, however, his crew "could bear no more." Columbus stood on the poop of the *Santa María* and confronted a shouting, gesticulating crowd of barefooted seamen in red stocking caps, who demanded that he turn back at once.

Columbus used "soft words." He spoke of the riches of the East. He urged them fervently to remember their duty to Ferdinand and Isabella. But in the end he was forced to agree that if no land appeared within three days, they would return to Spain.

The selection below narrates the critical events of the first ten days of October.

Wednesday, October 3   He followed his ordinary course; they went forty-seven leagues; he reckoned forty leagues to the men. Petrels appeared; there was much vegetation, some very faded and others very fresh and bearing something like fruit. They did not see any [other] birds, and the admiral believed that they had left behind the islands which he had depicted on his chart.

The admiral says here that it had not been his wish to keep beating about during the past week . . . when he saw so many indications of land, although he had information of certain islands in that region, in order not to delay, since his aim was to pass to the Indies. . . .

Thursday, October 4   He kept on his course to the west; they went, day and night together, sixty-three leagues; he reckoned forty-six to his men. There came to the ship more than forty petrels in a body, and two boobies, and a boy in the caravel hit one with a stone. A frigate bird came to the ship and a white bird like a gull.

Friday, October 5   He kept on his course; they made eleven miles an hour and in the night and day they went fifty-seven leagues, since during the night the wind freshened somewhat. He reckoned forty-five to his men. The sea was calm and smooth. "To God," he says, "many thanks be given." The air was very sweet and temperate; there was no vegetation; birds, many petrels. Many flying fish flew into the ship.

Saturday, October 6   He kept on his course westward; they went forty leagues in the day and night; he reckoned thirty-three to his men. On this night Martín Alonso said that it would be well to steer southwest by west, and the admiral thought that Martín Alonso did not say this on account of the island of Cipangu; and the admiral saw that if they missed it, they would not be able to reach land so soon, and that it was better to go at once to the mainland and afterward to the islands.

Sunday, October 7   He kept on his course to the west. . . . On this day, at sunrise, the caravel *Niña*, which went ahead as she was a fast sailer—and they all went as quickly as they could in order to be the first to sight land and secure the reward which the sovereigns had promised to whomsoever should first sight it—hoisted a standard at the masthead and

fired a lombard [small cannon], as a sign that they saw land. For so the admiral had ordered. He had also ordered that, at sunrise and at sunset, all the ships should join him, since these are the two periods when it is most possible to see for a distance, the mists clearing.

In the evening, the land which those in the *Niña* thought they had seen was not sighted, and a great flock of birds passed from the direction of the north to the southwest, which led him to believe that they were going to sleep on land or were, perhaps, flying from the winter which was about to come to the lands whence they came.

As the admiral knew that most of the islands which the Portuguese held had been discovered through birds, on this account the admiral decided to abandon the westward course and to steer west-southwest . . . for two days. He began to do so one hour before sunset. . . .

Monday, October 8   He navigated west-south-west, and day and night together they went about eleven and a half or twelve leagues. . . . They had a [calm] sea like the river of Seville. "Thanks be to God," says the admiral, "the breezes were softer than in April at Seville, so that it is a pleasure to be in them: they are so laden with scent." . . .

Tuesday, October 9   He sailed south-westward; he made five leagues. The wind changed and he ran to the west by north, and went four leagues. Afterward, in all, he made eleven leagues in the day and in the night twenty and a half leagues; he reckoned seventeen leagues to the men. All night they heard birds passing.

According to Columbus's chief recent biographer, Samuel Eliot Morison, the Pinzóns themselves pleaded with Columbus to turn back on October 9. After Columbus's death, when the Spanish government wished to deprive his descendants of their hereditary privileges, the government produced witnesses who stated that it was Columbus who became discouraged and Martín Alonso Pinzón who persuaded him to sail on. Most historians, including the official historian of the Spanish Crown in the sixteenth century, Oviedo, reject this testimony, which was presented at the *Pleitos de Colon* (Pleadings Concerning Columbus). Rugged Martín Alonso's reported advice to Columbus on how to handle the mutineers—"Hang half a dozen of them!"—sounds authentic, though.

Wednesday, October 10 He navigated westsouthwest. . . . They went fifty-nine leagues; he reckoned to the men forty-four leagues, no more.

Here the men could now bear no more; they complained of the long voyage. But the admiral heartened them as best he could, holding out to them bright hopes of the gains which they could make, and he added that it was vain for them to complain, since he was going to the Indies and must pursue his course until, with the help of Our Lord, he found them.

Chapter Five

‿♦‿

"TIERRA! TIERRA!"

The admiral, at ten o'clock in the night, being on the sterncastle, saw a light . . . like a small wax candle, which was raised and lowered.

— CHRISTOPHER COLUMBUS, *Journal*

SAN SALVADOR

On October 11, the day after the uprising on the *Santa
María*, there were more convincing signs of land, including a green branch with little red flowers. On a hunch,
Columbus changed his course back to due west, and the
ships flew before a northeast gale. He made a speech of
encouragement to the men that evening after the *Salve
Regina* ("Hail, Holy Queen"), the Latin hymn to the
Blessed Virgin Mary, was sung. Although he had given
orders that no night sailing should be done after the fleet
sailed seven hundred leagues beyond the Canaries, he now
navigated at night in order to get as far west as possible
in the three days allotted.

At 10 P.M., Columbus saw a mysterious light ahead. He
later claimed and received the reward of 10,000 maravedis
($700) annually for the first sighting of land on the basis
of this light. (A sailor who unsuccessfully contested Columbus's claim is said to have returned to North Africa
and become a Moslem because of his disappointment.)
Later that night, according to an eyewitness who testified
at the *Pleitos de Colon*, Rodrigo de Triana was keeping
watch on the *Pinta* and, "as the moon grew brighter, saw a
headland of white sand . . . [and cried] *'Tierra! Tierra!'*
['Land! Land!']"

Columbus's light was *not* a "luminous jellyfish" or "sea-
worms engaged in courtship"—two explanations which
have been suggested. It may have been imaginary, but it
may also have been real, one of the fires which the Indians
lit before their huts to keep off sand fleas. Such fires, it has
been shown, can be visible twenty-eight miles offshore.

The following selection describes the discovery of land
in the Western Hemisphere.

Thursday, October 11   He navigated to the west-southwest; they had a rougher sea than they had experienced during the whole voyage. They saw petrels and a green reed near the ship.

Those in the caravel *Pinta* saw a cane and a stick, and they secured another small stick, carved, as it appeared, with iron, and a piece of cane, and other vegetation which grows on land, and a small board. Those in the caravel *Niña* also saw other indications of land and a stick loaded with barnacles.

At these signs, all breathed again and rejoiced.

On this day, to sunset, they went twenty-seven leagues. After sunset he steered his former course to the west; they made twelve miles an hour, and up to two hours before midnight they had made ninety miles, which are twenty-two leagues and a half.

And since the caravel *Pinta* was swifter and went ahead of the admiral, she found land and made the signals which the admiral had commanded. This land was first sighted by a sailor called Rodrigo de Triana, although the admiral, at ten o'clock in the night, being on the sterncastle, saw a light.

It was, however, so obscured that he would not affirm that it was land, but called Pero Gutiérrez . . . and told him that there seemed to be a light, and that he should watch for it. He did so, and saw it. He [Columbus] said the same also to Rodrigo Sánchez of Segovia . . . and he [Rodrigo] saw nothing. . . .

SAN SALVADOR
(Watling I.)
Oct. 14 (GUANAHANÍ)

Oct. 12
Oct. 16
STA. MARIA DE LA
CONCEPCION *(Rum Cay)*

Oct. 18

FERNANDINA
(Long I.)

Oct. 19 *Oct. 20-24*
ISABELLA *(Crooked I.)* (SAMOETE)

Oct. 24
C. HERMOSO *(Fortune I.)*

Oct. 25
LAS ISLAS
DE ARENA
(Ragged Cays)

Oct. 26-27

Oct. 27
Oct. 28
Oct. 31

Nov. 19-20
Nov. 20

Nov. 13
Nov. 21
Nov. 14
Nov. 24

(Great Inagua I.)
(BABEQUE)

R. DE MARES
(Pto. Gibara)
PTO. DEL PRINCIPE
(Jucaro B.)
(Baricy B.)

LA MAR DE
NUESTRA SENORA
(Tanamo B.)

PTO. SANTO
(Pto. Baracoa)
C. ALPHA Y OMEGA
(C. Maisi)

JUANA
(Cuba)

Dec. 6

PTO. DE LA CONCEPCION
(Moustique B.)
TORTUGA
PTO. DE LA MAR DE STO. TOMAS
PTO. DE LA MAR DE STO. TOMAS
(Acul B.)
PUNTA SANTA
LA NAVIDAD
(Caracol B.)
MONTE CRISTI

PTO. DE SAN NICOLAS
C. DE LA ESTRELLA

Dec. 7
Dec. 7-14
Dec. 15-18
Dec. 19-20
Dec. 20-23
Dec. 25-Jan. 3
Jan. 4-5

HISPANIOLA
(BOHÍO)

N

KEY
ISLANDS NAMED BY COLUMBUS
(Modern Names of Islands)
(INDIAN NAMES)
OTHER PLACES NAMED BY COLUMBUS
(Modern names of other places)

After the admiral had so spoken, it was seen once or twice, and it was like a small wax candle, which was raised and lowered. Few thought that this was an indication of land, but the admiral was certain that they were near land.

Accordingly, when they had said the *Salve* . . . and . . . had all been gathered together, the admiral asked and urged them to keep a good lookout from the forecastle and to watch carefully for land; and to him who should say first that he saw land, he would give at once a silk doublet apart from the other rewards which the Sovereigns had promised, which were ten thousand maravedis annually to him who first sighted it.

[*Friday, October 12*] Two hours after midnight land appeared, at a distance of about two leagues from them. They took in all sail, remaining with the mainsail, which is the great sail without bonnets, and kept jogging, waiting for day, a Friday, on which they reached a small island of the [Bahamas], which is called in the language of the Indians *Guanahani* ["iguana," a reptile].

Immediately they saw naked people, and the admiral went ashore in the armed boat, and Martín Alonso Pinzón and Vincente Yañez [Pinzón], his brother, who was captain of the *Niña*. The admiral brought out the royal standard, and the captains went with two banners of the Green Cross, which the admiral flew on all the ships as a flag, with an F [for Ferdinand] and a Y [for Ysabella], and over each letter their crown, one being on one side of the ✠ and the other on the other.

When they had landed, they saw very green trees and much water and fruit of various kinds. The admiral called the two captains and the others who had landed, and Rodrigo d'Escobedo, secretary of the whole fleet, and Rodrigo Sánchez of Segovia, and said that they should bear witness and testimony how he, before them all, took possession of the island . . . for the King and Queen, his Sovereigns, making the declarations which are required.

The Spaniards landed on the western side of the island, which was sheltered from the wind. They wept and kissed the earth, begged Columbus's pardon for their doubts, and swore allegiance to him as their admiral and viceroy.

He drew the sword that hung at the side of his scarlet doublet and cried, "I hereby take possession of this island, to which I give the name of San Salvador, in the name of the King and Queen, my Sovereigns!"

San Salvador means "Holy Savior." Columbus chose this name because of his gratitude to God for "the immeasurable mercy of having reached it [the island]."

Soon many people of the island gathered there. What follows are the actual words of the admiral. . . .

"I," he says, "in order that they might feel great amity toward us, because I knew that they were a people to be delivered and converted to our holy faith rather by love than by force, gave to some among

them some red caps and some glass beads, which they hung round their necks, and many other things of little value. At this they were greatly pleased and became . . . entirely our friends. . . .

"Afterward they came swimming to the ships' boats, where we were, and brought us parrots and cotton thread in balls, and spears and many other things, and we exchanged for them other things, such as small glass beads and hawk's bells. . . . They took all and gave all, such as they had, with good will, but it seemed to me that they were a people very deficient in everything. They all go naked as their mothers bore them, and the women also, although I saw only one very young girl. . . .

"Some of them are painted black . . . and some of them are painted white and some red and some in any color that they find. Some of them paint their faces, some their whole bodies, some only the eyes, and some only the nose. They do not bear arms or know them, for I showed to them swords and they took them by the blade and cut themselves through ignorance. They have no iron. Their spears are certain reeds, without iron, and some of these have a fish tooth at the end, while others are pointed in various ways. . . .

"I saw some who bore marks of wounds on their bodies, and I made signs to them to ask how this came about, and they indicated to me that people [Caribs] came from other islands, which are near, and wished to capture them, and they defended themselves. And I believed and still believe that they come here from the mainland to take them for slaves.

"They should be good servants and of quick intelligence . . . and I believe that they would easily be made Christians, for it appeared to me that they had no creed. Our Lord willing, at the time of my departure I will bring back six of them to Your Highnesses, that they may learn to talk. I saw no beast of any kind in this island, except parrots."

The Bahama Islands stretch out for 630 miles in front of southern Florida, Cuba, and Hispaniola like a slanting picket fence. Columbus struck this "fence" near the middle, at San Salvador. But if he had not altered his course from west to west-southwest on October 7, to follow the birds migrating from North America to the West Indies, he would have sighted one of the northernmost Bahamas or the coast of Florida, and been swept north by the powerful Gulf Stream. He would not have found the gold of Hispaniola, which was the chief spur to later Spanish colonization.

INDIANS AND THE "MEN FROM HEAVEN"

Since he thought he was in islands near India, Columbus called the natives "Indians" (Spanish *Indios*, in Columbus's *Letter*, March, 1493). At first, he was surprised that they were not black, like the people he had seen in West Africa. But then he concluded that their copper color—that of the primitive Guanches of the Canary Islands—resulted from San Salvador's being in the same latitude as the Canaries.

Aristotle taught that peoples and products of the same latitude were similar.

Actually, these well-formed, black-haired natives of medium height were Tainos of the Arawak language group, whose ancestors had emigrated from South America. They were healthy, articulate, intelligent, and peaceful. Their low, broad foreheads came from having their skulls flattened by being pressed between two boards when they were infants. They wove cotton and made an excellent red pottery.

Spaniards and Indians regarded each other with wonder. Although the Tainos did not experiment as the West Africans had with the Portuguese—trying to rub the white off with spittle because they thought it was paint—they stroked the Spaniards' skin and beards, fell on their knees, and extended their arms in awe toward the "men from heaven."

Columbus's seamen, on the other hand, were astounded by the mild dispositions of their hosts, who brought them bread, water, cotton, gold ornaments—all they had. The Tainos's only weapons, wooden darts with fire-hardened points, were more for spearing fish than killing men. European intellectuals, reading about this harmless, naked people, decided they were relics of the Golden Age, or of the innocence Adam enjoyed (for six hours, according to theologians) before his Fall. The idea of the "noble savage," popular in the eighteenth century, originated here in the West Indies.

Columbus and the "practical" colonists who followed him had darker thoughts about the Tainos. In the third from last sentence of his entry for the day of discovery, Columbus had observed that the natives "should be good servants." In a passage below, he speculates that fifty Spaniards could reduce the entire island to slavery. Slavery and eventual extinction were to be the fate of the peaceful Tainos.

The selection below describes the Tainos, their fresh green island, their goods, their canoes (Columbus did not learn the Arawak word *canoa* until he reached Cuba), and an exploring trip Columbus made with the ships' boats around the north end of San Salvador.

Saturday, October 13 "As soon as day broke, there came to the shore many of these men, all youths . . . and all of a good height, very handsome people. Their hair is not curly, but loose and coarse as the hair of a horse; all have very broad foreheads and heads. . . . Their eyes are very lovely and not small. They are not at all black, but the color of Canarians, and nothing else could be expected, since this is in one line from east to west with the island of Hierro in the Canaries. Their legs are very straight, all alike; they have no bellies but very good figures.

"They came to the ship in boats, which are made of a tree trunk like a long boat and all of one piece. They are very wonderfully carved, considering the country, and large, so that in some forty or forty-five men came. Others are smaller, so that in some only a solitary man came. They row them with a paddle, like a baker's peel, and they travel wonderfully fast. If one capsizes, all at once begin to swim and right it, baling it out with gourds which they carry with them.

"They brought balls of spun cotton and parrots and spears and other trifles . . . and they gave all for anything that was given to them. And I was attentive and labored to know if they had gold, and I saw that some of them wore a small piece hanging from a hole which they have in the nose, and from signs I was able to understand that, going to the south or going round the island to the south, there was a king who had large vessels of it and possessed much gold. I endeavored to make them go there, and afterward saw that they were not inclined for the journey. . . . They said that there was land to the south and to the southwest and to the northwest. . . . So I resolved to go to the southwest, to seek the gold and precious stones.

"This island [Guanahaní] is fairly large and very flat; the trees are very green and there is much water. In the center of it, there is a very large lake; there is no mountain, and all is so green that it is a pleasure to gaze upon it.

"The people also are very gentle, and since they long to possess something of ours and fear that nothing will be given to them unless they give something, when they have nothing, they take what they can and immediately throw themselves into the water and swim [to the shore]. . . . They exchange things

even for pieces of broken dishes and bits of broken
glass cups. . . .

"In order not to lose time, I wish to go and see if
I can make the island of Cipangu. Now, as it was
night, they all went to land in their boats."

Sunday, October 14   "At dawn I ordered the
ship's boat and the boats of the caravels to be made
ready, and I went along the island [Guanahaní] in a
north-northeasterly direction, to see the other part,
which lay to the east, and its character, and also to
see the villages. And I soon saw two or three, and
the people all came to shore, calling us and giving
thanks to God.

"Some brought us water, others various eatables;
others, when they saw that I was not inclined to land,
threw themselves into the sea and came, swimming.
. . . One old man got into the [ship's] boat, and all
the rest, men and women, cried in loud voices: 'Come
and see the men who have come from heaven; bring
them food and drink.' Many came and many women,
each with something, giving thanks to God, throw-
ing themselves on the ground and raising their hands
to the sky, and then shouting to us that we should
land.

"But I feared to do so, seeing a great reef of rocks
which encircled the whole of that island [Guana-
haní], while within there is deep water and a harbor
large enough for all the ships of Christendom, the
entrance to which is very narrow. . . . Inside the

reef . . . the sea is no more disturbed than the water in a well. . . .

"I saw a piece of land, which is formed like an island although it is not one, on which there were six houses; it could be converted into an island [with a fort] . . . although I do not see that it is necessary to do so, for these people are very unskilled in arms, as Your Highnesses will see from the [ones] whom I caused to be taken in order to carry them off that they may learn our language and return. However, when Your Highnesses so command, they can all be carried off to Castile or held captive in the island itself, since with fifty men they would be all kept in subjection and forced to do whatever may be wished. . . .

"I examined the whole of that harbor, and afterward returned to the ship and set sail. I saw so many islands that I could not decide to which I would go first. . . . Finally I sought for the largest [Rum Cay] and resolved to steer for it, which I am doing. It is five leagues away from this island of San Salvador."

IN SEARCH OF GOLD

Beside Japan and China, Columbus had another objective, one that he *must* achieve if somehow the Eastern kingdoms eluded him. This was to discover gold. Fifteenth century Europe was suffering from a gold shortage, and Spain was especially affected. To justify the investment of Ferdinand

and Isabella, Columbus must try to find a source of gold comparable to the West African fields the Portuguese were tapping.

The six Tainos Columbus had kidnaped to serve as guides could make nothing of his inquiries about "Cipangu" and "Cathay"—but they could understand the gleam in the eyes of the "men from Heaven" at sight of their gold ornaments. They obtained these ornaments, chiefly nose pendants, by trade with other Tainos on Cuba. So they decided to direct their captors by the canoe route (the route with the shortest crossings over open water) to Cuba.

Columbus named and took formal possession of islands on the way: Santa María de la Concepción (Rum Cay), Fernandina (Long Island), Isabella (Crooked Island), and Juana (Cuba), named after the heir to the Spanish throne. Thus he gave the names in an order beginning with the Savior (San Salvador) and descending to his rulers, intending, says Ferdinand Columbus, "to honor both the spiritual and temporal powers." Except for San Salvador, named "in honor of God," he used feminine forms, as was the custom.

The selection below describes the search for gold on Santa María de la Concepción and Fernandina, the efforts of the guides to escape, and the appearance of a Taino hut.

Monday, October 15 "I stood off that night, fearing to come to anchor before daylight, as I did not know whether the coast was free from shoals. At daybreak I hoisted sail and . . . about midday . . . I arrived at the island. . . .

"To this island I gave the name Santa María de la Concepción, and about sunset, I anchored off the said point to learn if there were gold there, because those whom I had caused to be taken in the island of San Salvador told me that there they wore very large golden bracelets on the legs and arms. I can well believe that all that they said was a ruse in order to get away. It was nevertheless my wish not to pass any island without taking possession of it. . . .

"Tuesday . . . a large canoe was alongside the caravel *Niña,* and one of the men of the island of San Salvador, who was in her, threw himself into the sea and went off in it, and during the evening before midnight the other threw himself overboard. . . . [We] went after the canoe, which fled so that there was not a boat that could have overtaken it. . . . In the end it reached land and they left the canoe, and some of my company went ashore after them, and they all ran off like chickens. . . .

"[To] the caravel *Niña* . . . there now came from another direction another small canoe with a man who wished to barter a ball of cotton, and some sailors jumped into the sea and took him, because he would not come on board the caravel. I was on the poop of the ship . . . and I sent for him and gave him a red cap and some small beads of green glass, which I put on his arm, and two hawk's bells, which I put in his ears, and ordered his canoe, which was also in the ship's boat, to be given back to him and sent him ashore.

"After that I set sail to go to [another] large island [Long Island] which I saw to the west. . . .

Afterward, on land, when the [Indian] to whom I
had given the things mentioned . . . reached it, I saw
that all the rest clustered round him and that he was
dazzled and quite sure that we were good people
and that the one who had run away had somehow
wronged us and that accordingly we had carried
him off.

"It was to create this impression that I had so
acted with him, ordering him to be set free and giving him the presents, in order that we may be held
in his esteem so that when Your Highnesses again
send here, they may not be unfriendly. All that I
gave to him was not worth four maravedis [less
than four cents].

"So I departed at about ten o'clock . . . in order
to pass over to the other island . . . to which I gave
the name Fernandina. . . . These islands are very
green and fertile and the breezes are very soft, and
it is possible that there are in them many things of
which I do not know, because I did not wish to delay
in finding gold by . . . going about many islands. And
since these men [the Indians taken from San Salva-
dor] give these signs that they wear it on their arms
and legs, and it is gold because I showed them some
pieces of gold which I have, I cannot fail, with the
aid of Our Lord, to find the place whence it
comes." . . .

Tuesday and Wednesday [*sic*], *October 16* . . .
"There are here fish, so unlike ours that it is a marvel;
there are some shaped like dories [*gallus marinus,*

a species of fish], of the finest colors in the world, blue, yellow, red . . . and others painted in a thousand ways. . . . There are also whales. I saw no land animals of any kind, except parrots and lizards."

Wednesday, October 17 . . . "All these people [of Fernandina] are like those already mentioned. They are . . . as naked and of the same height, and they give what they have for whatever is given to them. And here I saw that some boys from the ships exchanged some little pieces of broken dishes and glass for their spears.

"The others, who went for the water, told me how they had been in their houses and that inside they were thoroughly swept and clean, and that their beds and coverings are like nets of cotton. They, that is, the houses, are all like tents and very high and with good chimneys, but among the many villages which I have seen, I have not seen one of more than from twelve to fifteen houses."

At the end of this entry, Columbus gave the first weather report from the Western Hemisphere: "It has rained, more or less, every day since I have been in these Indies." This was also his first use of the word "Indies" for these lands. He could have thought of them as islands in the Atlantic, like Antillia, but did not wish to.

NETS OF COTTON
The "beds . . . like nets of cotton" mentioned by Columbus above were hammocks (Arawak *hamaca*), a brilliant invention of the Tainos. Because of their coolness

and comfort, hammocks were quickly adopted by Spanish settlers in the West Indies and for use on shipboard. The hammock solved the able-bodied seaman's ancient problem of finding a place to sleep; it has only in this century been replaced by bunks in the British and United States navies.

The selection below, from Las Casas' *Historia de las Indias*, gives a detailed description of the hammock.

In . . . Hispaniola, these are called hammocks. They are shaped like slings, not woven like nets with the threads crossing obliquely, but the lengthwise threads [are] loose so that you can insert the fingers and the hand. And at a handsbreadth, more or less, these threads are crossed with other close-woven threads. . . .

These hammocks are a good [five and a half feet] in length. . . . At the ends [they] are finished off with many loops of the same threads . . . and, at the head, all the loops are connected as in the hilt of a sword, which at each end is fastened to the posts of the houses.

And thus the hammocks remain there swinging in the air. And since the good ones are [eight to eleven feet] wide, or more, one opens them when they swing as we should open a very large sling. One places oneself diagonally in [the hammock] . . . and thus there remains enough of the hammock to cover oneself with. And since it is never cold [in Hispaniola] that suffices. It is a restful thing to sleep in them . . . and . . . they are very clean.

THE ROAD TO CIPANGU

Columbus's next stop was Samoete (which he renamed Isabella), where his Indian guides assured him he would find a king who "wears . . . much gold." Columbus failed to find the king, but enjoyed the scent of flowers as from a greenhouse off the southern cape of the island. He called this headland of dark, weathered limestone cliffs *Cabo Hermoso* ("Cape Beautiful"). The country reminded him of Andalusia, a valley with luxuriant vegetation in southern Spain.

In the selection below, Columbus describes the island of Isabella, and states his plan to visit Cipangu, Cathay, and the Grand Khan.

Friday, October 19   "At dawn I weighed anchor and sent the caravel *Pinta* to the east-southeast, and the caravel *Niña* to the south-southeast, while I in the ship [*Santa María*] went to the southeast. I gave orders that they should follow these courses until midday, and that both should then change their course and rejoin me.

"And presently, before we had sailed for three hours, we saw an island to the east, toward which we steered, and all the three vessels reached it before midday, at its northern point, where there is an islet and a reef of rocks on its seaward side to the north and another between it and the main island. These men from San Salvador, whom I have with me, called this island 'Samoete,' and I named it Isabella. . . .

"There is no village, except further inland, where these men whom I have with me say that there is a king and that he wears much gold. Tomorrow I wish to go so far inland to find the village and to see or have speech with this king, who, according to the signs which these men make, rules all these neighboring islands and is clothed and wears on his person much gold, although I do not put much trust in what they say, both because I do not understand them well and because they are so poor in gold that any small amount which this king may wear would seem to be much to them. . . .

"If I arrive anywhere where there is gold or spices in quantity, I shall wait until I have collected as much as I am able. Accordingly I do nothing but go forward in the hope of finding these."

Sunday, October 21 "At ten o'clock . . . I went ashore, and there was there no village but only a single house, in which I found no one, so that I believe that they had fled in terror, because in the house were all their household goods. I allowed nothing to be touched, but only went with these captains and people to examine the island.

"If the others, which have been already seen, are very lovely and green and fertile, this is much more so, and has large and very green trees. There are here very extensive lagoons, and by them . . . wonderful woods, and . . . the whole island . . . is as green and the vegetation is as that of Andalusia in April. The singing of little birds is such that it seems that a man could never wish to leave this place; the flocks of parrots darken the sun, and there are large and small birds of so many different kinds and so unlike ours that it is a marvel.

"There are, moreover, trees of a thousand types, all with their various fruits and all scented. . . . I am the saddest man in the world because I do not recognize them, for I am very sure that all are of some value, and I am bringing specimens of them and also of the herbs.

"As I was thus going round one of these lagoons, I saw a snake [iguana], which we killed, and I am bringing its skin to Your Highnesses. When it saw us, it threw itself into the lagoon and we went in after it, for the water was not very deep, until we killed it with our spears. It is seven palms in length. . . .

"Here I recognized the aloe, and tomorrow I am resolved to have ten quintals [1,000 pounds] brought to the ship, since they tell me that it is very valuable. Further, going in search of very good water, we arrived at a village near here, half a league from where I am anchored. The inhabitants, when they saw us, all fled. . . .

"Afterward, some of the men among them came toward us and one came quite close. I gave him some hawk's bells and some little glass beads, and he was well content and very joyful. And . . . I asked him for water; and, after I had returned to the ship, they came presently to the beach with their gourds full, and were delighted to give it to us, and I commanded that another string of small glass beads should be given to them. . . .

"I was anxious to fill all the ships' casks with water here; accordingly, if the weather permit, I shall presently set out to go round the island, until I have had speech with this king and have seen whether I can obtain from him the gold which I hear that he wears.

"After that I wish to leave for another very large island, which I believe must be Cipangu [Japan], according to the signs which these Indians whom I have with me make; they call it 'Colba' [Cuba]. They say that there are ships and many very good sailors there.

"Beyond this island, there is another which they call 'Bohío' [Hispaniola] which they say is also very large. The others, which lie between them, we shall see in passing, and according to whether I shall find a quantity of gold or spices, I shall decide what is to be done. But I am still determined to proceed to the mainland and to the city of Kinsay and to give the letters of Your Highnesses to the Grand Khan, and to request a reply and return with it."

When Columbus reached the West Indies, he was confident that Japan lay just to the south or southwest, because fifteenth century maps (Martin Behaim's Globe of 1492, a Genoese map of 1457) showed Cipangu bordered by islands on the north. If he sailed southwest, he should arrive at Japan; if he missed Japan, he was bound to hit Cathay, most likely fabulous Kinsay (Hangchow), which was in about the same latitude as the Canaries.

Toscanelli's sea chart also depicted "innumerable islands," like pieces of a picture puzzle that have been jarred apart, around Cipangu. And the distance Columbus had come was almost exactly the distance Toscanelli gave for the voyage to Japan. When his Taino guides informed him that an island to the southwest called "Colba" was very large and rich, Columbus naturally assumed they were talking about Cipangu.

But, says Las Casas, the world was larger than Toscanelli and Columbus thought—and Columbus's voyage was, proportionately, shorter than he imagined. Cathay with its pearls, gold, and spices was still half the globe away. The gold nose plugs the Spaniards had collected were inconsequential; the one spice Columbus supposed he had found, the aloe (a purgative), was really a valueless agave plant; there were no gold-roofed palaces, only huts of wood and thatch.

Columbus remained confident, but a little puzzled. The beauty of tropical forests with their parrots and singing birds, the blue Caribbean, gleaming coral beaches and bright-colored fish, the fragrance of trees and flowers— these were the only riches he yet possessed after his three-thousand-mile journey.

Chapter Six

CATHAY
OR CIPANGU?

It is a rather contradictory thing to come from heaven and be going in search of gold.
—LAS CASAS, *Historia de las Indias*

Navigating through the Bahamas posed some problems. As Columbus explains below, the water around the islands is very deep, so that one must anchor close to shore—dangerously close, if it is night and the roadstead is new to the navigator. Also pinnacles of coral rock rise unexpectedly from the bottom to cut the anchor cable or punch holes in the ship's hull. Columbus did not wish to lose any of the seven anchors he carried in each vessel. In daylight, these coral formations can be seen through the clear water.

Columbus also gives a valuable complete list of the sails on the *Santa María*. The "bonnets" were extra rectangular sails attached below the mainsail. In later years the small topsail was enlarged and became more important in propelling sailing vessels.

The fleet sailed from Isabella (Crooked Island) through showers—the rainy season had set in—past the Ragged Cays, stepping-stone islets along the eastern edge of the Great Bahama Bank, which Columbus named *Las Islas de Arena* ("The Isles of Sand"). They arrived at Bahía Bariay (Bariay Bay) in eastern Cuba. The beach here was covered with mangrove trees. Soft, rounded mountains rose inland. There were "nightingales" singing (the Hispaniola mockingbird), there were yellow dogs which gave a kind of grunt instead of barking and were used chiefly for food—but was this Cipangu?

The selection below describes the voyage from Isabella (Crooked Island) southwest to Cuba, which Columbus thought would turn out to be Japan.

Wednesday, October 24 "This night, at midnight, I weighed anchor from the island of Isabella

[Crooked Island] . . . for the island of Cuba, which I hear from these people is very large and has much trade, and has in it gold and spices and great ships and merchants, and they indicated to me that I should steer west-southwest to go there. This I am doing, for I believe that . . . it is the island of Cipangu [Japan], of which marvelous things are recounted; and in the spheres which I have seen and in the drawings of [world maps], it is in this region.

"And I navigated until day to the west-southwest, and at dawn the wind fell and it rained, and so it was almost all night. I was thus with little wind until after midday, and then it began to blow very gently, and I set all my sails on the ship, the mainsail and two bonnets, and the foresail and spritsail, the mizzen, main topsail and the boat's sail on the poop.

"So I went on my course until nightfall. . . . And as it now blew hard . . . in order not to go in search of it [Cuba] at night . . . I decided to take in all sail, except the foresail, and to proceed under it. All these islands lie in very deep water, so that no bottom can be found beyond two lombard shots' distance, and then it is all patchy, one part being rocky and another sandy, and hence it is impossible to anchor safely, except when it is possible to see.

"After a short while, the wind became much stronger and I made a considerable distance, at which I felt misgivings, and as there were thick clouds and it was raining, I ordered the foresail to be furled, and that night we went less than two leagues."

On October 25 and October 26 Columbus sailed along "seven or eight islands in a row, all lying north and south." These were the Ragged Cays, which Columbus named *Las Islas de Arena*.

Saturday, October 27 They weighed anchor at sunrise from those islands, which he called Las Islas de Arena ["The Isles of Sand"], on account of the little depth of water which there was to the south of them for a distance of six leagues.

He made eight miles an hour to the south-south-west until one o'clock and they went about forty miles, and by nightfall they had gone twenty-eight miles more on the same course, and before night they saw land [Cuba]. They spent the night on watch while it rained heavily. . . .

Sunday, October 28 He went from there in search of the nearest point in the island of Cuba to the south-southwest, and he entered a very lovely river, very free from danger of shoals or of other obstacles, and the water all along the coast, where he went, was very deep and clear up to the shore. The mouth of the river was twelve fathoms deep. . . . He anchored . . . a lombard shot [800 to 1,000 yards] within it.

Any harbor that forms a river mouth is called *un rio* by Columbus.

The admiral says that he had never seen anything so beautiful. All the neighborhood of the river was full of trees, lovely and green, and different from ours, each one with flowers and fruit after its kind; there were many . . . small birds, which sang very sweetly. There were a great number of palms, different from those of Guinea [Africa] and from ours, of moderate height, and their feet had no bark, and the leaves were very large; they cover their houses with them. The land is very flat.

The admiral jumped into the boat and went to shore, and he came to two houses, which he believed to be those of fishermen, who fled in terror. In one of them he found a dog that never barked, and in both houses he found nets of palm fiber and lines and horn fishhooks, and bone harpoons, and other fishing tackle, and many fires in the houses. He believed that in each one of the houses many persons lived together. He commanded that none of these things should be touched, and so it was done.

The vegetation was as abundant as in Andalusia in April and May. He found much purslane [an herb] and wild amaranth [an herb]. He returned to the boat and went a good distance up the river, and it was, as he says, so great a joy to see that verdure and the trees and to hear the singing of the birds that he could not leave it to return. . . . The Indians whom he carried with him . . . told him by signs that there are ten large rivers, and that they cannot go round it [Cuba] in their canoes in twenty days. . . .

The Indians said that in that island there are gold mines and pearls; the admiral saw that the place was suited for them, and that there were mussels, which are an indication of them. And the admiral understood that the ships of the Grand Khan come there, and that they are large; and that from there to the mainland it is ten days' journey. The admiral called that river and harbor San Salvador ["Holy Savior"].

AMBASSADORS TO THE GRAND KHAN

Cuba thus far, even when viewed with the fervent faith of Columbus, did not look much like Cipangu. But perhaps these were the wilds of Cathay. Perhaps Kinsay, the fabulous "City of Heaven," lay only a short distance to the west. On October 29 Columbus sailed in that direction and reached the best harbor he had found yet, Rio de Mares ("River of Seas"—Puerto Gibara).

Now he checked the distance he had come from the Canaries—more than four thousand miles (a gross overestimate). Through the San Salvador Indians he asked the natives of Rio de Mares where they obtained their scanty gold ornaments, and they replied, *"Cubanacan"* ("mid-Cuba"), an inland district with a few unimportant mines.

"El Gran Can!" Columbus interpreted *Cubanacan*. That clinched it—he was in Cathay, certainly! These natives spoke of the "Grand Khan," while, according to his mistaken idea of the width of Asia, he had logged enough miles to carry him past Japan to China.

"It is a marvelous thing," comments Las Casas, "how if a man greatly desires something he imagines everything he sees and hears to be a sign of it." When Columbus tried to find Kinsay (Hangchow) and Zayton (Tsuen-chau or Chang-chau) by voyaging west of Rio de Mares and was driven back by opposing winds (a Caribbean norther was brewing), he noted, with the shift of wind, a cold current and put that down as another "sign" of Cathay (northern China).

So he prepared to send ambassadors to travel inland where he understood the Indians to say that the "Grand Khan" (actually their chief) resided. The selection below describes this embassy, which included Luís de Torres, official linguist of the fleet, and a sailor, Xerez, who had once visited a Negro king in Guinea. They carried Columbus's Latin passport, his Latin letter of credence, and a gift.

Thursday, November 1   At sunrise, the admiral sent the boats to land, to the houses . . . and they found that all the people had fled. . . . The houses . . . looked like tents in a camp, with no regular streets, but one here and another there. Inside, they were well swept and clean. . . . All were made of very beautiful palm branches.

[On October 29] they [had] found many images made like women and many heads like masks [in the houses]. . . . He did not know if they had them for their beauty, or whether they worship them. There were dogs that never bark . . . [and] wild birds, tamed. . . .

"These people [of Rio de Mares]," says the admiral, "are . . . the same . . . as the others . . . having no creed . . . but they say the *Salve* and the *Ave Maria* with their hands raised to heaven, as they are shown [by the Spaniards], and they make the sign of the cross. There is, moreover, one language for them all, and they are all friends, and I believe that all these islands are so and that they are at war with the Grand Khan. . . ."

"It is certain," says the admiral, "that this is the mainland [Cathay], and that I am . . . before Zayton and Kinsay. . . . And this appears clearly from the sea . . . yesterday, going to the northwest, I found that it was becoming cold."

Friday, November 2 The admiral decided to send two men, Spaniards [to the Grand Khan]: one was called Rodrigo de Xerez . . . and the other was a certain Luís de Torres . . . who . . . understood Hebrew and Chaldee and even some Arabic. With these he sent two Indians: one from . . . Guanahaní [San Salvador], and the other from [Rio de Mares]. . . .

He gave them strings of beads with which to buy food, if they were in need of it, and appointed six days as the time within which they must return. He gave them specimens of spices to see if they found any, and instructed them . . . what they were to say on behalf of the Sovereigns of Castile, how they had

sent the admiral to present letters on their behalf
and a gift.

They were also to learn of his estate, establish
friendship with him, and . . . gain knowledge of certain provinces and harbors and rivers . . . and learn
how far they were from this place, etc. . . .

Sunday, November 4 . . . The boatswain of the
Pinta said he had found cinnamon trees. The admiral
immediately went there and found that they were
not cinnamon. The admiral showed to some Indians
of that place cinnamon and pepper . . . and they recognized it, as he says, and indicated by signs that
there was much of it near there, toward the southeast.

Columbus wished to find spices as much as gold, because
in the fifteenth century spices were a source of great
wealth. Pepper, cloves, cinnamon, nutmeg, and ginger,
shipped to Europe from the East, brought profits of many
hundred per cent to importers.

From Indonesia to Egypt this trade was controlled by
Arab merchants; in the Mediterranean, by the Venetians;
and north of Italy, by the German merchants named Fug-
ger. But Portugal was about to reach the East by the sea
road around Africa and attempt to break these monopolies.
Columbus's backers hoped he would open a western route
to the spices, so much in demand as seasoning for a monoto-
nous diet.

He [Columbus] showed them gold and pearls,
and certain old men replied that in a place . . .
called "Bohío" [Hispaniola] there was a vast

amount, and that they wore it round the neck and on the ears and legs, and also pearls. He further understood that . . . there were large ships and merchandise, and that all this was to the southeast.

He also understood that far from there were men with one eye, and others with dogs' noses who ate men. . . . The admiral determined to return to the ship to await the two men whom he had sent. . . .

Columbus asked the Indians about one-eyed and dog-faced men because he had read in Mandeville's *Travels* that these monsters were found on islands off the coast of Asia. The Indians said yes, there were such men nearby—probably because they thought that was what Columbus wanted to hear.

Tuesday, November 6 Yesterday, in the night . . . the two men . . . came back, and they told [the admiral] that they had gone twelve leagues, as far as a village of fifty houses, where . . . there would be a thousand inhabitants. . . .

They said that they had been received with great solemnity . . . and that all . . . came to see them, and that they were lodged in the best houses. These people touched them and kissed their hands and feet . . . believing that they came from heaven. . . .

The most honorable persons of the village led them . . . to the chief house, and gave them two chairs on which they seated themselves, and they all sat on the ground around them [the two Chris-

tians]. The Indian who went with them told them
how the Christians lived and how they were good
people. Afterward the men went out and the women
entered, and sat in the same way round them [the
two Christians], kissing their hands and feet, fond-
ling them, trying to find if they were of flesh and
bone like themselves; they asked them to stay there
. . . for at least five days.

They exhibited the cinnamon and pepper and
other spices which the admiral had given to them,
and the others told them by signs that there was
much of it near there, to the southeast, but they
[the Indians] did not know if there was any in that
place. Having found that there was no indication
of any city, they returned. . . .

On the way [back] the two Christians found
many people, who were on their way to their villages,
men and women, with a brand in their hands, the
herbs for smoking which they are in the habit of
using. They found no village of more than five houses
on the way, and all gave them the same reception.

The ambassadors, having found a village of palm-
thatched huts instead of the Grand Khan's capital of Peking or golden Kinsay, had clearly failed. However, the
people they met on their return journey who carried
"herbs for smoking" introduced the Spaniards to a product
that, in the future, was to be even more in demand than
spices: tobacco.

The Indian smoker rolled the tobacco leaf into a "little bullet," thrust one end in his nose, inhaled the smoke a few times, then passed the "butt" on to a friend. The Indians claimed that stopping for a smoke at intervals on long journeys enabled them to overcome weariness.

Within forty years, Spanish colonists in the West Indies were smoking in imitation of the Indians, and by the seventeenth century the habit had spread throughout Europe. The passage above is the first mention of tobacco in history.

BLUEPRINT FOR EMPIRE

Although he lacked a formal education, Columbus was a man of original ideas. In the entry below he gives one of his ideas, an outline for a colonial empire for Spain. He explains to Ferdinand and Isabella how they can take advantage of the good-heartedness of the Indians by converting them, making them loyal Christian subjects, and exploiting their labor to obtain the products Columbus had found (or supposed he had found) in the "Indies."

Columbus himself took advantage of this innocent friendliness once more. After careening the *Santa María*—beaching it and tilting it first to one side, then to the other, to clean its bottom and recoat it with pitch—he seized more captives. Las Casas severely condemned this violation of "natural law" and the "law of nations." But early explorers looked on natives of the lands they discovered as scarcely human. They did not hesitate to kidnap them and present them as "free samples" to rulers—as proof of the explorers' having been in these new lands.

The selection that follows gives Columbus's blueprint for empire, and describes his taking the Indians at the end of his eleven-day stay at Rio de Mares. Two Indians later escaped; none of the rest survived the trip to Spain.

Monday, November 12 He left the harbor and
River of Mares . . . in order to go to an island which
the Indians, whom he carried with him, vigorously
affirmed was called "Babeque" [probably Great Inagua Island, north of the passage between Cuba and
Hispaniola], where they said . . . that the people
. . . gather gold on the shore at night with candles,
and afterward . . . with a mallet they make bars of
it. To go there, it was necessary to steer to the east
by south. . . .

He said that on the previous Sunday, the eleventh
of November, it had appeared to him . . . well to
take some persons from that river . . . to carry them
[home to Spain] to the Sovereigns, that they might
learn our language, in order to discover what there
is in the land, and that, on their return, they might
be tongues [interpreters] for the Christians and
adopt our customs and the things of our faith.

"Because I saw . . ." says the admiral, "that these
people have no creed and they are not idolaters, but
they are very gentle and do not know what it is to
be wicked, or to kill others, or to steal, and are un-
warlike and so timorous that a hundred of them
would run from one of our people . . . and they
believe . . . that there is a God in heaven, and they
are sure that we come from heaven, and they are
very ready to repeat any prayer that we say to them
and they make the sign of the cross.

"So your Highnesses should resolve to make them

Christians, for . . . if you begin, in a little while you will achieve the conversion of a great number of peoples to our holy faith, with the acquisition of great lordships [estates] and riches and all their inhabitants for Spain.

"For without doubt there is a very great amount of gold in these lands. . . . These Indians [from San Salvador] . . . say that . . . there are very large [gold] bracelets, pearls of great value, and an infinite amount of spices. And by this River of Mares . . . there is without doubt a very great quantity of mastic [a resin]. . . .

"And there is also a great amount of cotton here, and I believe that it would be marketed very well here, without bringing it to Spain, taking it only to the cities of the Grand Khan, which will doubtless be discovered, and to the many other cities of other lords who will delight to serve Your Highnesses, and where other things can be supplied from Spain. . . . And here there is also an infinite amount of aloe [lignaloes, a valuable plant used in medicine]. . . .

"And there is here at the mouth of this river the best harbor that I have seen so far, clear and wide and deep, and a good . . . situation for making a town and fort, and such that any ships whatever could lie alongside the walls, and the land very temperate and high, and very good waters.

"It was so that yesterday there came to the side of the ship a boat with six youths, and five came on board the ship; I ordered them to be kept and I will bring them with me. And afterward I sent to a house which is near the river to the west, and they brought seven head of women, small and large, and three children.

"I did this in order that the men might conduct themselves better in Spain, having women of their own land, than if they had not. . . . Having their women, they will be willing to do what is laid upon them, and also these women will do much to teach our people their language, which is one and the same throughout these islands of India . . . which is not the case in Guinea [Africa], where there are a thousand differing languages. . . .

"This night there came to the side in a canoe the husband of one of these women and father of three children, one male and two female, and asked if I would allow him to come with them and implored me greatly, and they are now all consoled, so that they must all be related. And he is a man of already forty-five years."

When Columbus observed, a few weeks later, that with his handful of seamen he could overrun "all these islands without . . . opposition," Las Casas accused him of inciting, by those and similar words, the Spanish "oppression and destruction" of the Indians. The Tainos were extinct by 1550.

THE PINTA DESERTS

Columbus now sailed east to go to Babeque, where the Indians said there was much gold. Thus he completed a

U-turn, begun when he reached San Salvador: he had swung south along the Great Bahama Bank to Cuba, and was now pointed back toward Africa.

When he tried to establish his latitude, he had more trouble with the North Star. While he was crossing the Atlantic it had shifted slightly from true north (see p. 118). Now it shot up in the sky "as high as in Castile," so that the puzzled Columbus, sighting it with his quadrant (the quadrant is an instrument for measuring the height, in degrees, of sun or stars), obtained a latitude of 42° for Cuba— the same as Chicago! He had gotten the same result November 2, and for the same reason: he mistook another star, Alfirk, for the North Star.

During the night of November 21 the *Pinta,* carrying nearly a third of Columbus's men and supplies, disappeared. Its commander, the veteran Martín Alonso Pinzón, had had arguments with Columbus earlier in the voyage about the course to be followed. Now Pinzón became impatient at the admiral's turning back to Cuba and sailed on eastward in the swift *Pinta* toward Babeque. He wanted to be the first to lay his hands on the gold which the Indians said abounded in that island.

After returning to Cuba, Columbus continued east along its north shore. He had examined oysters for pearls, but found none. He thought he discovered coconuts, as described by Marco Polo, but was mistaken. Now he found iron pyrites (fool's gold) in a river, hopefully collected samples for Ferdinand and Isabella, and tried to calm the panic among his San Salvador Indians over the cannibal Caribs, whose land they were approaching. Because he was seeking the luxuries of Asia, he failed to recognize the value of the different Caribbean products.

The selection below describes incidents of the voyage along the Cuban coast.

Wednesday, November 14 . . . [About one hundred miles east of Rio de Mares] he found a very deep inlet . . . and a good harbor and river, where he entered. . . . There he saw so many islands that he could not count them. . . . He assured the Sovereigns that the mountains . . . of these islands are in his opinion higher than any in the world, and more lovely and clear, with no cloud or snow, and very great depth of water at their foot.

And he says that he believes that these islands are those without number which in the [world maps] are placed at the end of the east. And . . . he believed that in them there were very great riches and precious stones and spices. . . . He gave the sea the name La Mar de Nuestra Señora ["The Sea of Our Lady"— Bahía Tánamo], and to the harbor . . . the name Puerto del Príncipe ["Port of the Prince"—probably Bahía Jucaro]. . . .

Some of [these islands] seemed to touch the sky, and they were fashioned like diamond points; others, over their highest point, have, as it were, a table on top. . . . They are all full of trees and are not rocky.

On November 19 Columbus sailed north-northeast from Tánamo Bay toward Babeque, but was forced back by opposing winds. At dusk, November 20, he changed his course to try once more to reach Babeque.

Wednesday, November 21 At sunrise, he steered to the east with a south wind; he made little progress, because the sea was against him. Up to the hour of vespers, he had gone twenty-four miles. Afterward, the wind changed to the east, and he went to the south by east, and at sunset he had gone twelve miles.

Here the admiral found that he was forty-two degrees from the equinoctial line [the equator], to the north, as he had been in the harbor of Mares. But here he says that he has abandoned use of the quadrant until he reaches land, in order that he could repair it. It was . . . his opinion that he was not so far distant [from the equator]. . . . It was, as he said, very hot. . . . From this heat . . . he argued that in these Indies and there where he was, there must be much gold.

This day Martín Alonso Pinzón, with the caravel *Pinta*, went away, without the permission and against the wish of the admiral, through greed, as he says, thinking that an Indian, whom the admiral had ordered to be placed in that caravel, would give him much gold; and he went away without waiting, without the excuse of bad weather, merely because he wished to do so; and the admiral says here: "He had done and said many other things to me."

Columbus suspected Pinzón of wishing to be the first to find gold, the first to return to Spain with news of the discovery of the Indies—of a rivalry so intense as to approach disloyalty. The tough veteran, on the other hand, may have considered the "foreigner" Columbus conceited and ungrateful for Pinzón's help in recruiting the crews.

Thursday, November 22 . . . On this night [during the dawn watch, 3 A.M. to 7 A.M.], Martín Alonso followed an easterly course in order to go to the island of Babeque, where the Indians say that there is much gold; he was within sight of the admiral and might have been some sixteen miles away. The admiral sailed within sight of land all night, and he caused some sail to be taken in and kept a lantern alight all night, because it seemed that [Martín Alonso] was coming toward him and the night was very clear and the wind light and good for him to come to him, if he wished.

Friday, November 23 The admiral steered all day [along the Cuban coast] toward the land to the south . . . which those Indians whom he had with him called "Bohío" [Hispaniola]. They said that this land was very extensive and that in it were people who had one eye in the forehead, and others whom they called *Canibales*. Of these last, they showed great fear, and when they saw that this course was being taken, they were speechless, he says, because those people ate them and because they are very warlike. . . .

Monday, November 26 . . . All the people who have been found up to this time have . . . the very greatest fear of those of Caniba . . . and they say that they live in this island of Bohío [Hispaniola] . . . and he believes that those of Caniba take these people, since they are very cowardly and know nothing of arms, from their lands and houses. . . .

He says that . . . he could not calm their terror; and they said that the people there [in Bohío] had only one eye and the face of a dog. The admiral believed that they were lying, and he thought that they must be under the dominion of the Grand Khan who captured them.

The Cariba or Caniba, a cruel, fierce race who gave their name to the Caribbean Sea and also gave us the word "cannibal," did eat their enemies. But the nearest Caribs were in Puerto Rico, not Hispaniola. The Caribs ("valiant men") came originally from South America.

ARRIVAL AT HISPANIOLA

The Grand Khan was not to be found, yet Columbus remained convinced that Cuba was Cathay. He was delayed for a week by bad weather in Puerto Santo ("Holy Port" —Baracoa), where the seamen washed their clothes in the river and enjoyed the native yams and squash. Then he sailed on to Cape Maisi, the eastern tip of Cuba. He later named this headland, after the letters that begin and end the Greek alphabet, Cape Alpha and Omega: "Cape Beginning (of the East) and End (of the West)." He considered it the eastern end of the *orbis terrarum*—the eastern end of China—balancing Cape St. Vincent, Portugal, at the western end.

Thus Columbus was still thinking in terms of the *orbis terrarum*, or Island of Earth, even while he was in the

midst of unheard-of new lands. *He* thought he had discovered a new route to old lands.

The selection below describes Columbus's third and last
attempt to reach Babeque, and the change of plans which
took him instead to Hispaniola. He landed at its western
end, modern Haiti.

Wednesday, December 5 . . . He [Columbus]
wished to go to the island of Babeque, which lay to
the northeast. . . . Yet he could not go to Babeque
. . . for the wind which he had was northeast. As
he so proceeded, he looked to the southeast and saw
land, and it was a very large island, of which . . .
he had already received information from the Indians,
who called it "Bohío" [Hispaniola], that it was populous. . . .

So, as the wind was northeast northerly, he decided to leave Cuba, or Juana, which up to then he
had regarded as being the mainland owing to its
extent, for he had gone fully 120 leagues along one
side of it. And he departed to the southeast by east.
. . . So up to sunset he made some eighty-eight miles,
which are twenty-two leagues, always to the southeast.

And as night was falling, he ordered the caravel
Niña, as she was fast, to go forward in order to examine the harbor before dark. Having arrived at
the mouth of the harbor, which was like the bay of
Cadiz, and as it was already night, she sent her boat,
carrying a light, to take soundings in the harbor.

Before the admiral came to where the caravel was lying to and waiting for the boat to make signals that she should enter the harbor, the light in the boat was extinguished. The caravel, as she saw no light, ran out and showed a light to the admiral. . . . Just at this point, those in the boat lit another light. The caravel went to it, and the admiral could not and remained all that night, beating about.

Thursday, December 6   At dawn, he found himself four leagues from the harbor. . . . He saw a lovely cape to the south by west, which he named Cabo de la Estrella ["Cape of the Star"], and it seemed to him that it was the last land of this island toward the south, and that the admiral was distant from it twenty-eight miles.

Another land appeared, like an island of small size, toward the east, at a distance of about forty miles. . . . He named [it] Isla de la Tortuga ["Turtle Island"]. . . .

At the hour of vespers he entered the said harbor and named it Puerto de San Nicolás, in honor of St. Nicholas, because it was his feast; and at its entrance he wondered at its beauty and goodness, and although he had greatly praised the harbors of Cuba, yet he says that beyond doubt this is not less to be praised but rather surpasses them, and there is none like it. . . .

At its entrance, to the southward, it forms a kind of promontory, and from there it extends about the same distance to the end, where there is a very lovely beach and a field of trees of a thousand kinds, all laden with fruit, which the admiral believed to be spices and nutmegs. . . . In the center of the beach there is a river. The depth of this harbor is marvelous. . . . The whole harbor . . . is fifteen fathoms deep and free from rocks. . . .

All this island seems to be more rocky than any that he had found hitherto; the trees are smaller and many of them are of the same kind as in Spain, such as [live] oaks and [arbutus] and others, and the same is true of the plants. . . . The air is very good and he had not found such cold as here, although it could hardly be described as cold, except in comparison with the other lands. . . .

Sunday, December 9 . . . Opposite [the] end [of the harbor] there are some plains, the loveliest in the world, and as fit for sowing as the lands of Castile, and indeed these are superior. For this reason, he named the island La Isla Española ["Spanish Island"].

The Tainos of Española (latinized to Hispaniola) were so shy that Columbus did not meet any of them face to face for a week. Signal fires flared on the hills of Tortuga at night, to warn of Carib raids; villages, built inland as a protection against the cannibals, who came by sea, were always deserted when the Spaniards arrived.

But on December 12, Columbus's men finally captured a beautiful girl "wearing only a gold nose plug," gave her clothes and presents on the *Santa María*, and sent her back to her people. At her report—she was a chief's daughter—

the Tainos came out of hiding, placing their hands on their heads as a sign of friendship, and began to trade with the Spaniards.

On the same day, Columbus erected a cross at Puerto de la Concepción ("Port of the Conception"—Moustique Bay), and took possession of Hispaniola for Ferdinand and Isabella.

THE GOLD MINES OF CIPANGU

When Columbus reached a spot about a third of the way east along the coast of Haiti, he found Indians wearing an unusual number of gold ornaments. From an "old man" he learned that "there were many islands near . . . in which very much gold was produced," and "that one island was all gold, and that in the others there was so great a quantity that . . . they smelt it and make bars and a thousand worked articles." The old man said these lands were to the east, so Columbus sailed on eastward that very night.

Two days later, December 20, he arrived at one of the most beautiful harbors in the West Indies, which he called Puerto de la Mar de Santo Tomás ("Port of the Sea of St. Thomas"—Acul Bay). Here he added false rhubarb (*Fausse rhubarbe*, with green berries and yellow roots) to his collection of comparatively worthless plants for Ferdinand and Isabella—still overlooking the maize, rubber, and tobacco beneath his nose. But here also he received an invitation and a handsome gift from chivalrous King Guacanagarí, the *cacique* (Arawak for "chief") for all northwestern Haiti. And he heard of the gold mines of "Cipangu."

The following selection describes these events, the last of which changed Columbus's expedition from a "costly failure" to a success.

Thursday, December 20 Today, at sunset, he entered a harbor [Acul Bay] which was . . . most beautiful and . . . in which all the ships of Christendom could lie. From the sea its entrance appears to be impossible to those who have not entered it, owing to some reefs of rocks . . . which are not in a continuous line but are some here and some there, some being out to sea and others near the land.

Consequently one has to be on watch to enter by some gaps which there are, very wide and good, so that it is possible to enter without fear; and all is very deep, seven fathoms, and when the reefs are passed, within it is twelve fathoms. The ship can be fastened with any cable against whatever winds may blow. . . .

From that harbor, a very large valley appeared, all cultivated; it ran down to the harbor from the southeast and was all fenced in by very lofty mountains, which seemed to touch the sky, and which were very beautiful, full of green trees, and without doubt there are there loftier mountains than the island of Tenerife in the Canaries. . . .

Saturday, December 22 At daybreak he set sail to proceed on his way, in search of the islands which the Indians told him had much gold, and some of which they declared to have more gold than earth. The weather was not favorable, and he was obliged to anchor again [in Acul Bay], and he sent the boat to fish with the net.

The lord of that land [King Guacanagarí], who had his village near there, sent him a large canoe, full of people, and in it one of his principal servants, to ask the admiral to go with the ships to his land, telling him that he would give him all that he possessed. He sent with that servant a [belt] which had hanging from it, in place of a purse, a mask of which the two ears, which were large, the tongue and the nose were of beaten gold. . . .

They came up to the boat and gave the [belt] to a ship's boy, and then came in their canoe alongside the ship to perform their embassy. Some part of the day passed before he understood them. . . . Finally, by means of signs, he succeeded in understanding their invitation. He resolved to leave for that place on Sunday.

Guacanagarí's village was behind Caracol Bay, which lay just east of the next cape (Cape Haitien). The cotton belt he sent was four fingers wide, embroidered with red and white fishbones.

Sunday, December 23   For lack of wind the admiral could not leave with the ships for the land of that lord [King Guacanagarí] who had sent to ask him . . . to come, but . . . he sent the boats with people [seamen] and the secretary [of the fleet].

While these were on their way, he [Columbus] sent two of the Indians, whom he had with him, to the villages which were near there . . . and they re-

turned with . . . news that in the island of Española
there was a great quantity of gold . . . and they told
him that there he might have as much as he wished.
Others came who confirmed the statement . . . and
. . . showed him the method which they used to collect it.

All this the admiral understood with difficulty,
but yet he regarded it as clear that in those parts
there was a very great quantity of gold and that, if
the place where it was procured were found, he would
get it very cheaply. . . . During the three days he was
in that harbor he had secured good pieces of gold,
and it could not be believed that they brought it
there from another land.

"Our Lord, Who holds all things in His hand,
be pleased to aid me and to give whatever may be
for His service." These are the words of the admiral. . . .

Monday, December 24   Before sunrise he weighed
anchor with a land breeze. Among the many Indians
who had come yesterday to the ship and who had indicated to them that there was gold in that island
and had named the places where it was collected, he
saw one who seemed to be . . . more attached to him.
. . . He flattered this man and asked him to go with
him to show him the mines of gold.

This Indian brought another, a friend or relation,
with him, and among the other places which they
named where gold was found, they spoke of Cipangu,

which they call "Cibao," and they declared that there was a great quantity of gold there, and that the cacique carries banners of beaten gold, but that it is very far to the east.

Cibao was central Hispaniola, where the gold was mined. But Columbus interpreted it as Marco Polo's Cipangu of gold-roofed palaces, and joyfully sailed east to celebrate Christmas in Japan. His voyage was over a route the ship's boat had explored the day before; therefore, he was less watchful than usual as the *Santa María* and *Niña* entered the calm waters of Caracol Bay near midnight.

Chapter Seven

SHIPWRECK
AND STORM

I could have endured this storm with less anguish if my life alone had been in danger.... What caused me infinite grief and anxiety was the thought that after Our Lord . . . had crowned [this enterprise] with victory ... His Divine Majesty should now seek to hinder this with my death—a fate that I could have borne more easily did it not also threaten the people I had brought with me.

—CHRISTOPHER COLUMBUS, quoted
in Ferdinand Columbus's *Life of
the Admiral Christopher Columbus*

Near midnight, Christmas Eve, the new moon was just
setting behind Cape Haitien. It cast a dim light over the
dark expanse of Caracol Bay, across which two ships
moved slowly, their sails limp. On the *Santa María* the
crew of forty, including the officer of the watch and the
helmsman, were asleep. Only a little gromet (cabin boy),
wakened by the helmsman and given the tiller, stood below
the quarterdeck and steered by the compass.

Everyone was exhausted by two nights of visits from
over a thousand sightseeing Indians. There seemed no danger—little wind, a calm sea, a course reconnoitered by the
ship's boat yesterday. The little gromet gripped the heavy
wooden bar and heard the rudder creaking in its socket. He
did not hear the faint sound of surf or see the thin line of
foam, curling over a submerged coral reef dead ahead.

The water parted before the ship's prow with scarcely
a ripple. Very gently the *Santa María*, carrying over half of
Columbus's remaining men and supplies, grounded on the
West Indian reef.

Then the boy shouted. Columbus ran on deck. His men
tumbled out behind him, including the negligent officer of
the watch, Juan de la Cosa.

Quickly Columbus gave orders. Juan de la Cosa—carry
an anchor into the boat towed astern and cast the anchor
into the deep water behind the ship! Pass the cable forward
—attach it to the ship's windlass—attempt to "kedge" the
ship off, that is, wind in the cable and pull the vessel back-
ward off the coral. Hurry!

Juan de la Cosa jumped hastily into the boat with some
of his friends—but rowed off toward the *Niña* to save himself! Meanwhile the swell of the sea swung the *Santa María*
broadside upon the reef, each wave lifting the hull, then
dropping it on the sharp coral. The seams began to open.

The selection below describes the wreck of the *Santa*

María and the help given Columbus the next morning by chivalrous King Guacanagarí.

Tuesday, December 25, Christmas Day   He navigated with little wind yesterday from the Sea of St. Thomas toward Punta Santa [Cape Haitien], from which he was distant one league. . . . At eleven o'clock at night . . . he decided to lie down to sleep, because for two days and a night he had not slept. As it was calm, the sailor who was steering the ship decided to go to sleep, and he left the steering to a young ship's boy, a thing which the admiral had always strictly forbidden during the whole voyage. . . .

The admiral felt secure from banks and rocks, because on Sunday, when he sent the boats to that king [Guacanagarí], they had passed a full three leagues and a half to the east of Punta Santa, and the sailors had seen all the coast and the shoals from Punta Santa to the east-southeast for a full three leagues, and they had found where it was possible to pass, which he had not done during the whole voyage.

Our Lord willed that at midnight, as they had seen the admiral lie down and rest, and as they saw that it was a dead calm and the sea was as in a bowl, all should lie down to sleep, and the rudder was left in the hand of that boy, and the currents carried the ship upon one of those banks; the sea breaking on them made so much noise that it could be heard and seen, although it was night, at a full league's distance.

The ship went upon it so gently that it was hardly noticed. The boy, who felt the rudder ground and heard the sound of the sea, shouted, and at his cries the admiral came out and was so quick that no one had yet realized that they were aground.

Immediately the master of the ship [Juan de la Cosa], whose watch it was, came out, and the admiral told him and the others to launch the boat which they carried at the stern, to take an anchor and throw it out astern, and he with many others jumped into the boat, and the admiral thought that they were doing what he had ordered them to do. They only thought of escaping to the caravel [*Niña*], which was lying half a league to windward.

The caravel would not take them aboard, therein acting rightly, and on this account they returned to the ship, but the boat of the caravel reached her first.

When the admiral saw that they were running away . . . and that the water was growing shallower and the ship was now lying broadside on to the sea . . . he ordered the mast to be cut and the ship to be lightened as far as possible to see whether they could draw her off. And as the water became shallower still, he was unable to save her, and she lay on her side, broadside on to the sea, although there was little or no sea running, and then the seams opened, but the ship remained whole.

The admiral went to the caravel, in order to place the crew of the ship in safety on the caravel, and as a light breeze was now blowing from land, and there also still remained much of the night and they did not know how far the banks extended, he hung off until it was day and then went to the ship from within the line of the bank.

He had first sent the boat ashore with Diego de Harana of Cordova, alguacil [marshal] of the fleet, and Pero Gutiérrez, butler of the royal household, to inform the king who on Saturday night had sent him an invitation and asked him to come to his harbor with the ships, and who had his town about a league and a half away from the bank.

When he [the king] heard the news . . . he . . . sent all his people from the town, with many large canoes to unload the ship. This was done and everything was taken from the decks in a very short space of time. So great was the haste and diligence which that king showed!

And he in person, with his brothers and relatives, was active both on the ship and in guarding what was brought to land. . . . From time to time he sent one of his relatives in tears to the admiral, to console him, telling him that he must not be troubled or annoyed, that he would give him whatever he possessed.

The admiral assures the Sovereigns that nowhere in Castile could he have been able to place everything in greater security, without the loss of a shoestring. He [the king] commanded everything to be placed near the houses, while some houses which he wished to give were emptied, that there everything might be placed and guarded. He ordered armed men to be set round everything to keep watch all night.

"He and all the people with him wept . . ." says the admiral.

Columbus called de la Cosa's disobedience "treason," not "cowardice." In calm weather, with the coast in sight, the danger was not great. De la Cosa, a part owner of the *Santa María*, must have had some personal grudge against Columbus.

Having only one ship, the *Niña*, Columbus now abandoned his plan to explore the rest of Hispaniola's north shore and decided to return directly to Spain.

THE FIRST COLONY

Although Guacanagarí showed the "courtesy, honesty, dignity, and simplicity" of an ideal "noble savage," it was the arrival of Indians from the east with many pieces of gold leaf which cheered Columbus. The newcomers paddled their canoes to the *Niña* and happily exchanged their gold for hawk's bells—shiny tinklers, like sleigh bells, much better for the Indians to dance by than their wooden rattles.

Guacanagarí himself offered four pieces of gold as large as a man's hand, and promised that he would "cover everything with gold" before Columbus departed. He mentioned the mines of Cibao (Columbus heard "Cipangu"), and at a banquet placed his gold crown on Columbus's head. In return, Columbus gave the cacique a necklace of bright-colored glass beads, a scarlet cloth, and a silver ring.

Columbus now decided the wreck had been ordained by heaven so that he would find gold here and be forced to establish a colony. There was not room for all the men in the *Niña*. Thirty-nine were to remain in a settlement on shore opposite the reef—including the fleet's marshal, interpreter, and secretary. Most of those who stayed behind were eager volunteers whose eyes reflected the gleam of the gold pieces. Columbus hoped they would find spices (in addition to the West Indian chili) and the source of the gold.

The following selection describes the founding of the first European colony in the Western Hemisphere. Columbus named it La Navidad (Christmas) after the day of their arrival.

Wednesday, December 26   Today at sunrise the king . . . came to the caravel *Niña*, where the admiral was, and, almost in tears, told him that he must not be grieved, for he would give him whatever he had . . . and as many canoes as they needed to . . . unload the ship . . . as had been done yesterday. . . .

While the admiral was talking with him, another canoe came from another direction, which brought certain pieces of gold, which they wanted to give for a hawk's bell. . . . So while the canoe had not yet reached the ship's side, they . . . showed the pieces of gold, crying *"chuque, chuque,"* meaning hawk's bells, for they almost go crazy for them. . . . They called the admiral and asked him to have a hawk's bell kept until next day, since they would bring him four pieces of gold as large as the hand. The admiral rejoiced to hear this. . . .

The king was greatly delighted to see the admiral

joyful and understood that he desired much gold,
and he told him by signs that he knew where there
was very much . . . near there, and that . . . he would
give him as much gold as he might desire. . . . He
[the king] explained . . . that in Cipangu, which
they called "Cibao," it was in such quantity that
they regard it as of no account, and that he would
bring it from there. . . .

The admiral was greatly pleased and consoled . . .
and the grief and pain which he had suffered . . .
for the loss of the ship was assuaged, and he recognized that Our Lord had caused the ship to run
aground there in order that a settlement might there
be formed.

"And," he says, ". . . in truth it was no disaster,
but rather great good fortune; for . . . had I not
run aground there, I should have kept out to sea
without anchoring at this place . . . and . . . I should
not have left people here. And had I desired to leave
them, I could not have given them so many supplies
. . . nor the material needed for making a fort.

"And . . . many of the people who are with me
have asked . . . that I give them permission to remain.

"Now I have ordered a tower and fortress to be
built . . . and a large moat, not that I believe it to
be necessary . . . for I take it for granted that with
these men whom I have with me I could subdue all
this island, which I believe to be larger than Portugal

and with more than twice the population. . . . It is right, however, that this tower should be built . . . in order that they may realize the skill of the people of Your Highnesses and what they can do, so that they may serve them with love and fear.

"So they have boards [from the wrecked *Santa María*] with which to construct the whole fortress, and provisions of bread and wine for more than a year, and seeds to sow, and the ship's boat and a caulker [to make the seams of a ship or boat watertight] and a carpenter and a gunner and a cooper [to make or repair casks], and many men among them who are very zealous in the service of Your Highnesses. . . .

"Thus, then, all has happened greatly to the purpose that a beginning may be made. . . ."

All this the admiral says, and he adds . . . that the ship [the *Santa María*] was very slow and not suited to the work of discovery. . . . And he says that he trusts in God that on his return, which he intended to make from Castile, he would find a barrel of gold, which those whom he had left there should have obtained by barter, and they would have found the gold mine and the spices, and in such quantity that the Sovereigns, within three years, would undertake . . . the conquest of the Holy Places.

"For so," he says, "I protested to Your Highnesses that all the gain of this my enterprise should be expended on the conquest of Jerusalem, and Your

Highnesses smiled and said that it pleased them, and that without this they had that inclination. . . ."

Monday, December 31   On this day, he [Columbus] concerned himself with ordering water and wood to be taken in for his departure for Spain, in order to give speedy news to the Sovereigns, that they might send ships to discover what remained to be discovered. . . .

And he says that he did not wish to depart until he had seen all that land . . . toward the east and gone along all the coast, in order to learn also the length of the journey from Castile there . . . for the purpose of bringing stock and other things. But, as he was left with only one ship, it did not seem to him reasonable to expose himself to the dangers which he might encounter in the course of discovery; and he complained that all this evil and inconvenience was the result of the caravel *Pinta* having parted from him.

Wednesday, January 2   He landed in the morning in order to take leave of King Guacanagarí . . . and he gave him one of his shirts. And he showed the power which the lombards had . . . for . . . he ordered one to be loaded and fired at the side of the ship [the *Santa María*] which was aground. This was as a result of a conversation concerning the Caribs, with whom they were at war; and he [King Guacanagarí] saw how far the lombard carried and how it pierced the side of the ship. . . .

He also had the people of the ships arm themselves and engage in a sham fight, telling the cacique that he was not to fear the Caribs even if they should come. All this the admiral says that he did, that the king might regard the Christians whom he left as friends and might be frightened and have fear of them. . . .

The admiral . . . left in that island of Española . . . thirty-nine men in the fortress, and . . . they were very friendly with that King Guacanagarí. Over them, as his lieutenants, he left Diego de Harana, a native of Cordova, and Pero Gutiérrez, butler of the king's dais . . . and Rodrigo d'Escobedo, a native of Segovia . . . with all his powers which he held from the Sovereigns.

He left with them all the merchandise which the Sovereigns commanded to be bought for purposes of barter . . . that they might . . . exchange it for gold. . . . He left them also bread, biscuit for a year, and wine, and much artillery, and the ship's boat, in order that they . . . might go . . . to discover the mine of gold . . . and a place . . . where a town might be established, because this was not a harbor after his heart. . . . The gold which they brought there came . . . from the east, and the more they were to the east, the nearer they were to Spain.

He left them also some seeds to sow, and his officials, the secretary and the alguacil [marshal], and with them a ship's carpenter and a caulker and a good gunner . . . and a cooper, and a doctor, and a tailor, and all, as he says, seamen.

Before departing, Columbus gave the colonists excellent advice (which they did not follow): to obey his lieutenants, to show reverence toward their benefactor Guacanagarí, and not to injure the Indians, especially the women. Instead, after Columbus's departure, they split into quarreling cliques and roved the countryside, robbing and abusing the people until the Indians rose and slaughtered them all. Guacanagarí disclaimed responsibility for the killing, and apparently was guiltless.

THE GULF OF ARROWS

Columbus sailed east from La Navidad on January 4. Two days later, near Monte Cristi, Pinzón, like a bad penny, turned up. Columbus had received reports in La Navidad that the *Pinta* was in a river farther east, and had sent a "loving letter" to Pinzón, trying to entice him back, but the messenger had not found the caravel.

Now the *Pinta* sailed up from the east, and after both the vessels anchored, Pinzón came to Columbus's cabin, full of excuses for parting from the fleet "against his will." He had a satisfied and knowing look in his eyes, gold in his pockets, and six captives—four Indian men and two women—in his ship. Columbus righteously freed the captives (Pinzón's, not his own), changed the name of a stream from Pinzón River to River of Grace (to indicate Pinzón was pardoned, although he didn't deserve to be), but had to allow Pinzón to keep his gold. Pinzón may have traveled to the Cibao district himself. He was said to have retained half the gold his crew collected.

Columbus said he "did not know the cause of the arrogance and disloyalty with which he [Pinzón] had used him during the voyage." Pinzón *had* deserted to look for gold on Babeque (Great Inagua Island), had found none there, but then had reached Hispaniola ahead of Columbus and discovered plenty.

In spite of the strained relations, Columbus was glad to have a second ship for the return voyage, and even decided to explore more of the north coast of Hispaniola before departing for Spain. He spent two days at Monte Cristi (just beyond Haiti, in what is now the Dominican Republic), where he caulked the *Niña* and found virgin gold in the Rio Yaque del Norte. Then he sailed on east.

On January 12, 1493, he rounded a headland and anchored in a bay he afterward named Golfo de las Flechas ("The Gulf of Arrows"—Samaná Bay). The next day a landing party from the *Niña* encountered fifty-five Indians "more ugly . . . than any . . . seen" before. Their faces were stained with charcoal, and they brandished palm clubs and bows and arrows in a very businesslike fashion.

They were not Caribs, as Columbus thought, but they had adopted Carib weapons—and Carib manners. They did not for one instant look upon the seven Spaniards who confronted them on the beach as "men from heaven." Almost immediately, as described below, a dangerous conflict broke out.

Sunday, January 13   He did not go out of this harbor because there was no land breeze with which to do so. . . . He sent the boat to land at a beautiful beach, in order that they might take *ajes* [yams] to eat, and they found some men with bows and arrows,

with whom they paused to talk, and they bought
two bows and many arrows, and asked one of them
to go to speak with the admiral in the caravel, and
he came.

The admiral says that he was more ugly in appearance than any whom he had seen. He had his face
all stained with charcoal . . . he wore all his hair
very long and drawn back and . . . gathered in meshes
of parrots' feathers, and he was as naked as the others.
The admiral judged that he must be one of the Caribs
who eat men. . . .

He questioned him concerning the Caribs, and
the Indian indicated to him that they were near there
to the east [i.e., in Puerto Rico]. . . . He ordered food
to be given to the Indian, and gave him pieces of
green and red cloth, and glass beads . . . and sent
him back to shore. . . .

When the boat reached the shore, there were behind the trees quite fifty-five men, naked, with very
long hair, as women wear their hair in Castile. At
the back of the head they wore tufts of parrot
feathers and feathers of other birds, and each one
carried his bow. The Indian [whom Columbus had
entertained] landed and caused the others to lay
aside their bows and arrows and a short stick, which
. . . they carry in place of a sword.

Afterward they came to the boat and the people
from the boat landed, and they began to buy from

them their bows and arrows and other weapons, because the admiral had ordered this to be done.

When two bows had been sold, they would not give more, but prepared rather to assault the Christians and capture them. They went running to collect their bows and arrows, where they had laid them aside, and came back with ropes in their hands, in order . . . to bind the Christians.

Seeing them come running toward them, the Christians, being on guard, as the admiral always advised them to be, fell upon them, and they gave an Indian a great slash on the buttocks and they wounded another in the breast with an arrow. When they saw that they could gain little, although the Christians were not more than seven and they were fifty and more, they turned in flight . . . one leaving his arrows here and another his bow there. The Christians . . . would have killed many of them, if the pilot who went with them as their captain had not prevented it.

Afterward the Christians returned to the caravel with their boat, and when the admiral learned of it, he said that on the one hand he was sorry, and on the other hand not, since they would be afraid of the Christians, for without doubt . . . the people there are, as he says, evildoers, and . . . were those from Carib . . . [who] eat men. Accordingly, if the boat which he had left with the thirty-nine men in the fortress and town of La Navidad should come there, these would be afraid to do any ill to them.

The next day these Indians—Arawaks called Ciguayos—came back to trade as though nothing had happened. Their king visited the *Niña* and promised Columbus a gold crown, which he had delivered the following day.

There was much gulfweed in the bay; because of his theory of the origin of gulfweed (see p. 119), Columbus concluded that other islands were not far east, and that it was only about 1,480 miles to the Canaries.

Before leaving, Columbus seized four Ciguayo youths to take to Spain.

HOMEWARD BOUND

Columbus had read in Marco Polo the same story Mandeville told (see p. 48), of an island inhabited only by women. The Arawak Indians also had a myth about a hero named Guagugiona who had filled one island, Matinino (identified with Martinique), with women. Columbus heard this tale from his captives, connected it with Marco Polo, and planned to visit Matinino to take on ballast—and to kidnap several women as further proof that he had indeed reached Marco Polo's East.

The following selection describes how Columbus set out for Matinino and also for the "island of Carib" (Puerto Rico), but had to change his course.

Wednesday, January 16   He set out from the gulf, which he called Golfo de las Flechas ["The Gulf of Arrows"], three hours before day with a land breeze, and afterward with a west wind, steering to the east by north, in order to go . . . to the island of Carib [Puerto Rico], where lived the people of whom all those islands and lands were in so great fear, because it is said that with their innumerable canoes they go about all those seas and . . . eat the men whom they can take. . . . Some Indians, of the four whom he had taken yesterday in the harbor of Las Flechas, had shown him the course.

After having gone . . . sixty-four miles, the Indians indicated to him that the island lay to the southeast. He wished to take that route, and ordered the sails trimmed, and after having gone two leagues, the wind became stronger, very good for going to Spain.

He observed among the people that they began to grow sad because they were turning aside from the direct course, owing to the fact that both caravels were making much water, and that they had no remedy save in God. He was forced to abandon the course which he believed led to the island, and he went about to the direct course for Spain, northeast by east. . . .

The Indians told him that by that route he would find the island at Matinino, which is said to be peopled by women without men, and which the admiral greatly desired to visit, in order, as he says, to take to the Sovereigns five or six of them. But he doubted whether the Indians knew the course well, and he could not delay on account of the danger from the water which the caravels were shipping.

But he says that it was certain that there were these

women, and that at a certain time of the year men
came to them from the island of Carib. . . . And if
they gave birth to a boy, they sent him to the island
of the men, and if to a girl, they kept her with
them. . . .

After having lost sight of the cape on the island
of Española which he called Sant Théramo [Balandra
Head, Samaná Bay] . . . he went twelve leagues to
the east by north [in the open sea]. He had very
good weather.

A GREAT STORM

The "direct course for Spain" which Columbus first followed (northeast by east) would have brought him
"home" among arctic icebergs. It was a blunder, like
Columbus's underestimate of the width of the Ocean Sea
on the outward voyage. Yet, in the end, this blunder also
worked out well: the ships reached the latitude of Ber-
muda, the latitude of the westerlies, in the shortest possible
time by beating north against the northeast trade wind.

Then Columbus had second thoughts. The rough sea
did not allow him to sight accurately with quadrant or
astrolabe, but he judged—correctly—that the North Star
was as high in the sky as it was at Cape St. Vincent, Portugal. He now steered due east, and thus followed the
route recommended today as the best one for sailing vessels
bound for Europe from the Caribbean.

Meanwhile the weather had grown much colder, the
wind stronger. *Niña* and *Pinta* flew across a broken, green-
ish-blue sea, under a glittering winter sky. They logged
150–200 miles a day—until the wind attained gale force,

the sky darkened, and lightning flared in the north-north-east. They were in the storm track of the North Atlantic, and heading into a major disturbance.

A cold air mass, moving south from the arctic, was colliding with a warm air mass from the tropics. On February 12 the ships began to labor in heavy seas. By the night of February 13 they were being overtaken by one of the storm's three "fronts" (two cold, one warm). Foaming green waves crashed on the decks, and *Pinta* disappeared in the blackness.

Niña ran before the gale, carrying just a small mainsail, slung low. The helmsman, drenched by the water which poured through the rudder port, struggled desperately to keep the ship from being swung broadside and swamped.

Columbus and his men turned to prayer. It was doubtful if any of them would see Spain again.

The following selection describes the storm near the Azores.

Tuesday, February 12   He navigated to the east at six miles an hour this night, and by daybreak he . . . began to experience heavy seas and stormy weather. . . .

Wednesday, February 13   After sunset, until day, he experienced great difficulty from the wind and from the very high sea and the stormy weather. It flashed with lightning three times to the north-northeast; he said that this was an indication of a great storm which would come from that direction or against him. For most of the night, he went with bare poles; afterward he hoisted a little sail and went fifty-two miles. . . .

This day the wind moderated a little, but presently it increased, and the sea became terrible, and the waves met each other, so that they strained the ships. He made fifty-five miles. . . .

Thursday, February 14 This night the wind increased and the waves were terrible, one meeting another, so that they crossed and held back the ship, which could not go forward or come out from the midst of them, and they broke over her. He carried the mainsail very low, merely in order to escape to some extent from the waves; he so went for three hours and ran twenty miles.

The sea and wind increased much, and seeing that the danger was great, he began to run before the wind where it bore him, as there was no other recourse.

Then the caravel *Pinta,* in which was Martín Alonso, also began to run before the wind and disappeared, although all night the admiral made flares and the other vessel answered, until, as it seems, she could do so no more owing to the violence of the storm and because she was very far out of the course of the admiral. This night the admiral went to the northeast by east fifty-four miles. . . .

The sun having risen, the wind and sea were greater, the cross waves more terrible. He set only the mainsail and carried it low, in order that the ship

might get out from among the waves which crossed
and threatened to sink her. He followed the course
to the east-northeast, and afterward, to the east by
north . . . and . . . made seven leagues and a half.

Columbus and his men now placed chick-peas in a cap,
marking one with a cross, and drew to see who would go
on a pilgrimage to the shrine of Santa María de Guadalupe
if the ship were saved. The lot fell to Columbus. They
drew again for a pilgrimage to the shrine of Santa María
de Loreto, and when a seaman chose the marked pea,
Columbus promised to pay the cost of the journey. In a
third drawing, for a pilgrimage to the Shrine of Santa Clara
de Moguer, the lot once more fell to Columbus.

After this, the admiral and all the people made a
vow that, on reaching the first land, they would all
go in their shirts [as a sign of humility] in procession
to pray in a church dedicated to Our Lady. Besides
the general vows . . . each one made his own indi-
vidual vow, because no one expected to escape . . .
owing to the terrible storm. . . .

It contributed to increase the danger that the ship
was short of ballast, as the cargo had been lightened,
the stores of food having been already eaten and the
water and wine drunk; owing to his eager desire to
avail himself of the fine weather which they experienced among the islands, the admiral did not provide
ballast, intending to have it taken in at the island of
the women, where he proposed to go. The remedy

which he [had] found for this need was, when they were able to do so, to fill the casks full of sea water.

COLUMBUS'S FEARS

At the height of the storm Columbus sat in his cabin, which tilted wildly with the pitching of the ship, and wrote a brief, hasty account of his discoveries. The selection below describes what he did with this account (which has never been recovered) and the fears he experienced at this time.

Thursday, February 14 (continued)   Here the admiral writes of the reasons which caused him to fear that Our Lord willed that he should perish there, and of other reasons which gave him hope that God would bring him in safety, so that such news, as he was bearing to the Sovereigns, should not be lost.

It seemed to him that the great desire which he had to bring this momentous news and to show that he had been proved a truth-teller in what he . . . had offered to discover, inspired him with the greatest fear that he would not achieve this. . . .

On the other hand, he drew comfort from the blessings which God had shown to him in giving him so great a victory, in the discovery of what he had discovered. . . . So he must believe that He would finish what had been begun and bring him to safety . . . so that he says that he should not have feared the said storm. "But [my] weakness and anxiety," he says, "did not permit [my] mind to be soothed."

He says further that he felt also great anxiety for two sons whom he had in Cordova at school, for he would leave them orphaned . . . in a strange land, and that the Sovereigns would not know the services which he had rendered to them on that voyage and the most favorable news which he was bearing to them, so that they might be moved to succor his sons.

For this reason, and that their Highnesses might know how Our Lord had given him the victory in all that he desired in the matter of the Indies . . . he took a parchment and wrote on it all that he could about all the things he had found, earnestly begging whomsoever might find it to carry it to the Sovereigns. This parchment he enclosed in a waxed cloth . . . and he commanded a large wooden barrel to be brought, and placed it in it, without anyone knowing what it was, for they thought that it was some act of devotion, and he ordered it thrown into the sea. . . .

TREACHERY IN THE AZORES

In winter, the Azores, Portuguese possessions, are cold and rainy. But on February 15, when Columbus sighted southernmost Santa Maria, and on February 18, when he finally succeeded in anchoring off the north coast of this small, rocky island, it looked almost as good to his crew as San Salvador had. Some of his men first thought it Castile, others Portugal, others Madeira; but Columbus, an uncanny dead-reckoning navigator, plotted the course and said they had reached the Azores.

On February 16, as the *Niña* struggled through the dying tempest, Columbus had his first sleep in several nights. He found himself "very crippled in his legs owing to having been constantly exposed to the cold and water" —and suffered from arthritis for the rest of his life.

The Azores turned out to be a perilous berth. Around the horizon the dark Atlantic clouds still lowered. A boisterous wind threatened to shift and drive the *Niña* from its unprotected anchorage upon the granite shore. And the temporary captain of the island, an angry young man named Castañeda, sought to make a name for himself by arresting Columbus and his crew as Spanish poachers who had been illegally trading in Guinea.

The selection below describes how half the conquerors of the Ocean Sea spent their first night back on European soil inside a prison—and how a trap was set for Columbus.

Tuesday, February 19   After sunset, there came to the shore three men of the island [Santa Maria] and called. He [Columbus] sent the boat to them and they came in it, and brought fowls and fresh bread and . . . other things sent by the captain of the island, who was called Juan de Castañeda, who sent word that he . . . would come at daybreak. . . .

And because on the previous Thursday, when he found himself in the anguish of the storm, they had made a vow . . . that in the first land where there was a house of Our Lady, they would go in their shirts, etc., he decided that one-half of the people should go in fulfillment to a small house, which was near the sea and like a hermitage, and that he would go

afterward with the other half. Seeing that the land
was safe and trusting in the offers of the captain
and in the peace which there was between Portugal
and Castile, he asked the three men to go to the village and have a priest come to say mass for them.

They [half the crew] went in their shirts, in fulfillment of their pilgrimage, and as they were at
prayer, there fell upon them the whole village on
horse and on foot, with the captain, and made them
all prisoners.

Afterward the admiral, being without suspicion,
awaited the boat in order to go to fulfill his pilgrimage with the remaining people. At eleven o'clock,
when he saw that they did not come, he suspected
that they had been kept or that the boat had been
wrecked. . . .

He weighed anchor and sailed directly toward the
hermitage, and saw many men on horseback, who
dismounted and entered the boat in arms and came
to the caravel to arrest the admiral. The captain stood
up in the boat and asked a safe conduct from the
admiral. He replied that he granted it to him, but
what change was this that none of his people were
in the boat? And the admiral added that if he would
come and enter the caravel, all would be done as he
desired.

The admiral was trying to draw him on board
with smooth words, that he might take him and re-

cover his men. He did not believe that he was breaking faith by giving him a safe conduct, since the
captain had offered peace and security and had not
kept his word.

The captain would not trust himself on board. . . .
Having seen that he would not come to the caravel,
the admiral asked him to explain why he detained
his men, adding that this would offend the King of
Portugal, and that in the territory of the Sovereigns
of Castile the Portuguese received much honor. . . .
And since the Sovereigns had given him letters of credence for all the princes and lords and men in the
world, he would exhibit them to him, if he would
come on board. . . . And he showed them to him at a
distance. . . .

Then the captain replied that he and the others
did not recognize the King and Queen of Castile, or
their letters, nor did they fear them; on the contrary,
they would have him understand that this was Portugal, saying this in a rather threatening manner.

When the admiral heard this, he was greatly concerned . . . He thought that some dispute must have
occurred between the one kingdom and the other
after his departure, and he could not refrain from
making that reply to them which was proper. . . .
He . . . swore that he . . . would not land . . . until
he had carried a hundred Portuguese to Castile and
depopulated all that island.

And so he returned to anchor in the harbor where he had first been, as the weather and wind were very unsuitable for him to do anything else.

Furious, Columbus anchored within sight of the treacherous village (Anjos), but the next day his anchor cables snapped. He had to put out to sea to escape being wrecked on the coast. He headed east for São Miguel Island, could not reach it because of rough weather, and the next afternoon returned to Santa Maria for further negotiations with the scornful Castañeda.

Friday, February 22   Yesterday he anchored at the island of Santa Maria in the place . . . where he had first anchored, and immediately there came a man who called from some rocks . . . opposite . . . saying that they should not go away. . . . Afterward came the boat with five sailors and two priests and a notary; they asked for a safe conduct, and when it had been given by the admiral, they came on board the caravel and as it was night they slept there, and the admiral showed them such honor as he could.

In the morning they required him to show them his commission from the Sovereigns of Castile. . . . The admiral felt that they did this in order to make some show of not having done wrong . . . because they had not been able to take the person of the admiral . . . but . . . found that the game was not turning out well for them. . . .

Finally, in order to recover the people whom they held, he had to show to them the circular letter of credence from the Sovereigns . . . and they went ashore satisfied, and afterward released all the people with the boat, from whom he learned that if they had taken the admiral, they would never have let him go free. . . .

LISBON HARBOR—A ROYAL INTERVIEW

Having been prevented by a fresh gale from collecting wood and stone ballast, Columbus left the Azores on February 24 and sailed east toward Cape St. Vincent. This bitter winter, ships were wind-bound at Lisbon for months, while the great southern port of Genoa was frozen over on Christmas. On February 27 another Atlantic tempest overtook the *Niña* and pounded the caravel for six days as it slowly passed. Winds of hurricane strength split the sails; the terrible cross waves seemed to toss the light caravel into the air.

The *Niña* limped into Lisbon Harbor, and then Columbus faced another danger. King John II, the "Perfect Prince" who had rejected Columbus's "Enterprise" eight years earlier, would not enjoy hearing now of his triumph in the service of a rival. If Columbus were too tactless, would the trim, energetic king, who knew well how to use the dagger in his belt, yield to the pleas of courtiers and have the "upstart" assassinated?

The selection below describes Columbus's narrow escape from the second, most violent storm, and his touchy interview with the king of Portugal.

Wednesday, February 27   This night and day he went out of his course, owing to contrary winds and heavy waves and sea, and he found himself 125 leagues from Cape St. Vincent. . . . He was very grieved at so great a storm when he was on the threshold of home.

Sunday, March 3   After sunset, he navigated on his course to the east. There came a squall which tore all the sails, and he saw himself in great peril. . . . He cast lots to send a pilgrim . . . who should go in his shirt to Santa Maria de la Çinta in Huelva, and the lot fell on the admiral. They all also made a vow to fast on bread and water on the first Saturday after they reached land.

He made sixty miles before the sails were torn; afterward they went with bare poles, owing to the great storm of wind and sea which from two sides broke over them. They saw indications that they were near land; they found themselves to be very near Lisbon.

Monday, March 4   Last night they experienced a terrible storm, so that they thought that they were lost owing to the seas which came upon them from two sides, and the winds, which seemed to lift the caravel into the air, and the water from the sky and lightning from many sides. . . . So he went until the first watch [7 P.M.], when Our Lord showed him land, the sailors seeing it.

This land was the rockbound coast of Portugal, dead ahead. If Columbus had not found a single remaining storm squaresail in the locker and set it on the foremast to keep the ship offshore, the *Niña* and probably the entire crew would have been lost.

And then, in order not to come to it until he might know it and see if he could find some harbor or place where they might be safe, he hoisted the mainsail . . . and went some way, although with great danger, keeping out to sea . . . until day. . . .

When day came, he recognized the land as being the rock of Cintra, which is close to the river of Lisbon [the Tagus], where he resolved to enter, because he could do nothing else, so terrible was the storm which prevailed at the town of Cascaes, which is at the entrance of the river.

He says that the people of the place were all that morning offering up prayers for them, and after he was within, the people came to see them in wonder that they had . . . escaped. And so at the hour of terce [probably 9 A.M.], he came to rest at Rastelo within the river of Lisbon.

In the harbor, Columbus was questioned by Bartholomew Dias, whose triumphant return from the discovery of the Cape of Good Hope he had witnessed five years before. Then John II, learning of Columbus's arrival, invited Columbus to visit him at a monastery thirty miles from Lisbon. After the people of the city had come out to the *Niña* (March 6 and 7) and marveled at the Indians, Columbus rode through this capital of many memories—perhaps past the convent chapel where he had met his wife

Dona Felipa, perhaps past his and Bartholomew's old shop
—to a royal interview.

Saturday, March 9   Today he left . . . to go where
the King was, which was in the *Valle del Paráyso*,
nine leagues from Lisbon. As it was raining, he could
not reach there until night.

The King commanded the chief persons of his
household to receive him very honorably, and the
King also received him with great honor, and showed
him much favor and commanded him to be seated.
He spoke very amiably . . . and he showed that he
was very pleased that there had been a successful con-
clusion to that voyage . . . but he understood that
according to the capitulation [Treaty of Alcáçovas,
1479] which had been made between the Sovereigns
[Ferdinand and Isabella] and himself, that conquest
belonged to him.

To this the admiral replied that he had not seen
the capitulation nor did he know anything save that
the Sovereigns had commanded that he should not
go to Elmina or any part of Guinea, and that so it
had been proclaimed in all the ports of Andalusia
before he set out on his voyage.

The King graciously answered that he was sure
that in this matter there would be no need for arbi-
trators; he handed him over as a guest to the prior of
Crato, he being the most important personage who
was there, and from him the admiral received much
honor and favor.

Shrewd King John was already preparing his claim to the West Indies on the ground that the Ocean Sea south of the Canaries and west of Africa was in the Portuguese sphere of influence. But according to the contemporary Portuguese chronicler Rui de Pina, the king's surface friendliness was a pretense. He was enraged at Columbus's triumph and at his self-assured manner.

He tried to catch Columbus by having one Indian arrange a map of the West Indies with dried beans, then "accidentally" scattering the beans and asking another Indian to reassemble them—to see if the maps would be alike. They were alike—and the second had even more detail than the first. Thereupon, according to de Pina, the king struck himself on the breast and cried passionately, "O man of poor understanding! Why did I let slip from my hand an enterprise of such great importance!"

BACK FROM AMERICA

Columbus refused King John's offer to send him home by land, over lonely roads, and sailed from Lisbon March 13. Rounding steep Cape St. Vincent, he fired a salute to the Christian martyr after whom it was named. There was the rocky shore to which he had swum, after being wounded in the naval battle, seventeen years ago.

Next appeared the low-lying Atlantic coast of Spain, with its pines and its marshlands, looking out on the mysterious Green Sea of Darkness which had awed men for two thousand years, but would awe them no longer.

And there was the break in the coastline, the sluggish tidal river Saltés, the Rio Tinto branching off to the right, and the red tile roofs of sleepy Palos. It was noon, March 15, 1493.

Columbus and his crew, with their captive Indians, would have great tidings to tell. The Sovereigns at Barcelona would be waiting to hear. The voyage was ended, but the process of spreading the news was just beginning.

Anchors were let go. Columbus sat in his cabin for a quiet twenty minutes and finished his *Journal*. The following is the concluding entry.

Wednesday, March 13 Today at eight o'clock, at ebb tide and with a north-northwest wind, he weighed anchor and set sail to go to Seville.

Thursday, March 14 Yesterday, after sunset, he followed his course to the south, and before sunrise he found himself off Cape St. Vincent, which is in Portugal. Afterward he steered to the east, to go to Saltés, and he went all day with a light wind, until now when he is off Faro.

Friday, March 15 Yesterday, after sunset, he went on his course until day with little wind, and at sunrise he found himself off Saltés, and at midday, with a rising tide, he entered by the bar of Saltés into the port [Palos] from which he had departed on the third day of August in the previous year.

And so he says that here ends this writing, save that he intended to go to Barcelona by sea, having had news that their Highnesses were in that city, and this in order to give them an account of all his voyage which Our Lord permitted him to perform, and to which He had inspired him. . . .

"Of this voyage," says the admiral, "I know that this has been miraculously shown to be so, as can be understood from this writing, by the many notable miracles which He has shown forth on the voyage and for me, who for so long a time was in the court of Your Highnesses with the opposition of so many chief persons of your household and against their opinion, for they were all against me, regarding this undertaking as a jest. And I hope in Our Lord that it will be the greatest honor for Christendom to have been brought forth so easily."

These [words above] are the last words of the Admiral Don Christopher Columbus concerning his first voyage to the Indies and their discovery. . . .

Thanks be to God.

The *Pinta* missed the Azores and landed in northern Spain, above Portugal. Pinzón had written the king and queen, but they refused to see him before Columbus arrived. The *Pinta* reached Palos March 15, just behind the *Niña*, but Martín Alonso, worn out by hardships and heartbroken over the snub, died a few days later.

Now came Columbus's hour of glory. He rode to Seville, then, in a procession that included seven Indians carrying red and green parrots, fishbone belts and masks, and samples of gold to Barcelona. There Ferdinand and Isabella received him in court beneath a canopy of cloth of gold, before a great throng. Dour Ferdinand smiled, and Isabella graciously made her admiral be seated beside them and Prince Juan. A joyous *Te Deum* was chanted in the royal chapel.

Columbus's *Letter* on his first voyage, a brief summary of the *Journal* which he had composed on the way back as a public announcement of his discoveries, was copied for royal officials and printed in Barcelona. In 1493–94, a Latin translation went through nine editions in Rome, Paris, Basel, and Antwerp.

Princes, prelates, and scholars read the *Letter*, lauded the heroic Genoan, and began to ask questions. Europe was fascinated by the "Indies." Not everyone agreed with Columbus that he had been to Japan, however.

Could these warm "islands in the Western Ocean," with their yams, canoes, gold, *hamacas*, and naked natives be something else? If so, what else?

Chapter Eight

A NEW WORLD

In past days I wrote very fully to you of my return from the new countries. . . . And it is lawful to call it a new world, because none of these countries were known to our ancestors.
—AMERIGO VESPUCCI, Mundus Novus *letter, 1503*

Five years before Columbus sailed for the Indies, Peter Martyr, a talented and idealistic young Italian, had been invited to come to the Spanish court and introduce Renaissance learning there. By accident he became the chief early historian of Columbus's voyages.

"Promise that you will send me regular information about happenings at the Spanish court," urged Cardinal Sforza, one of Peter Martyr's Roman friends.

Peter Martyr agreed. In fulfillment of that promise, he started to write, in October, 1494, a series of letters called the "Ocean Decades" (*De Rebus Oceanis et Orbe Novo Decades*), in Latin, about the most exciting events of the times—the voyages of Columbus and his successors. The first *Decades* were printed in 1504; additional *Decades* appeared in 1516 and 1530. They established Columbus's reputation as a discoverer and aroused Europe to the importance of the new lands.

Like any good journalist, Peter Martyr coined a striking phrase to describe the hero of his history. In a letter dated November 1, 1493, he called Columbus "that discoverer of a new world."

But what did Peter Martyr mean by his "new world" (*novus orbis*)? In other letters Peter Martyr said that Columbus had gone to "the western antipodes," "the western hemisphere," or "a new hemisphere." "New world" *could* mean a new world of Asiatic islands, or even a peninsula of Asia, hitherto unknown to Europe. It need not be a "world" separate from the only known world, the *orbis terrarum*.

Two of Peter Martyr's references to Columbus's voyage printed below—especially the second reference—show

that he was not certain. His famous phrase pointed up but
did not solve the problem of what lands Columbus had
found.

A few days afterward, there returned from the
western Antipodes a certain Christopher Columbus,
a Genoese, who had with difficulty obtained from my
Sovereigns three ships [to sail to] this country, because the things he was saying were thought to be
fables. He returned bearing samples of many precious
things, especially of gold, which those regions naturally produce.

(*Letter to Count Borromeo, May 14, 1493*)

A certain Columbus has voyaged to the western
Antipodes, all the way to the shore of India (as he
believes). He has discovered many islands; these are
thought to be the ones mentioned by cosmographers,
beyond the eastern Ocean and adjacent to India. I do
not wholly deny it, although the size of the globe
would seem to suggest otherwise. For there are not
lacking those who think the Indian shore is separated
from the end of Spain by a small space.

However that may be, they say that he has discovered great things. He brings proofs of what he
says; he promises that he will find greater things.

Enough for us that the hidden half of the globe
is brought to light. Also the Portuguese daily go
farther and farther below the equator. So shores
hitherto unknown will soon be made accessible. For

one [nation] in emulation of the other sets out on labors and enormous perils.

(*Letter to the Archbishop of Braga, October 1, 1493*)

THE END OF THE EAST

Columbus himself had no doubt about where he had been. For nearly ten years he had endured the scorn of courtiers for his Enterprise—but he had proved them all wrong. He had sailed by the western route to the "end of the East." What else could those lands be but the eastern end of the *orbis terrarum?*

Even after his third voyage (1498–1500), on which he discovered South America, Columbus remained confident that he had reached the "end of the East." Only then he added another possibility: that he might have reached that part of the East in which the earthly paradise itself—the Garden of Eden—was located (see p. 50). With the fervent medievalism which was combined with Renaissance accuracy of observation in his character, he suggested that the great volume of fresh water he saw pouring from the Orinoco River into the Gulf of Paria might have its source in the four rivers of the earthly paradise. If it did not, he admitted, it must then drain a "vast land," a continent.

(After relating Columbus's ideas about the earthly paradise in his *Decades*, the humanist Peter Martyr dismissed them with the comment, "But we have had enough of these things which to me seem fabulous.")

Columbus also used such phrases as "another world" and "a new heaven and a new earth" in letters describing the regions he had discovered. But by these phrases he meant simply other parts of Asia not previously known to Europe.

The passages below, from Columbus's letters, contain these phrases, and present his theory of the location of the earthly paradise.

All this was of no avail with certain persons who were determined . . . to malign the enterprise [the third voyage]. . . . Nor did it avail to say that I have never read that princes of Castile had ever gained lands beyond their own borders and that this land here is another world from that in which the Romans and Alexander and the Greeks labored to gain dominion.

Columbus describes his crossing the Atlantic to the island of Trinidad and thence to Venezuela—"Little Venice," so named by a later explorer, Ojeda, from a native village built on piles on the shores of a gulf. Then Columbus states his theory that the world is not perfectly round but pear-shaped; it is "everywhere very round except where the stalk is . . . and . . . this part . . . is the highest and nearest to the sky." The highest part of the earth is found "at the end of the East . . . where end all the land and islands."

But the earthly paradise, "from which flow four of the chief rivers of this world, the Ganges . . . the Tigris and Euphrates . . . and the Nile," is also located at "the end of the East," at the highest point of the earth. And in crossing the Atlantic, Columbus found by some astronomical calculations that "the ships went rising gently toward the sky." He therefore concludes that in Venezuela he has arrived at the threshold of the earthly paradise.

I believe . . . [there] are great indications of the earthly paradise [in the Gulf of Paria, Venezuela]

. . . for I have never read or heard of so great a quantity of fresh water so coming into and near the salt. . . . If it be not from the earthly paradise that this river [the Orinoco] comes, it originates from a vast land, lying to the south, of which hitherto no knowledge has been obtained. But I am much more convinced in my own mind that there . . . is the earthly paradise. . . .

May it please Our Lord to forgive the persons who have calumniated [made false statements about] . . . so excellent an undertaking. . . . They do not consider . . . that no princes of Spain ever won lands beyond their own borders, except now that Your Highnesses have here another world.

(*Columbus's Letter to Ferdinand and Isabella,
on the Third Voyage, October 18, 1498*)

In order somewhat to mitigate the grief that death [of her son, Prince Juan] has brought upon her [Isabella], I entered upon a new voyage to a new heaven and a new earth, which up to then had lain hidden.

(*Columbus's Letter to Dona Juana de Torres,
on the Third Voyage, October, 1500*)

MUNDUS NOVUS

A less important explorer but a persuasive and entertaining writer, Amerigo Vespucci was the first to explain correctly what the lands found by Columbus were. He gave his explanation in connection with South America, down whose coast he voyaged in 1501–02 on a Portuguese expedition, perhaps as far as southern Argentina.

In a letter to his former employer, Lorenzo Piero di Medici, the following year, Vespucci emphasized that South America was a continent, that it stretched far south of the equator, where geographers had taught there was only water or uninhabited land, and that it was "more populous . . . than our Europe, or Asia, or Africa."

It should therefore, said Vespucci, be called "a new world"—in contrast to the old world of "Europe . . . Asia . . . [and] Africa."

Vespucci neither confused his reader with fancies about the earthly paradise nor made implausible attempts to connect the new land with Cathay or Cipangu. No world map showed an Asiatic peninsula extending as far south as he claimed to have sailed. His letter omitted important facts, such as the identity of the commander of the expedition, and contained suspicious exaggerations and mistakes. But it hammered home the theme of a region "entirely new" —"over an eighth of the sphere, never seen by our ancestors."

When this letter, in a Latin translation titled *Mundus Novus* ("New World"), ran through nine editions and became a bestseller across Europe, Amerigo Vespucci's name was inextricably linked with the southern continent discovered by Columbus in 1498.

Amerigo Vespucci himself is an enigma to historians. A shrewd, self-assured Florentine merchant, he did not go to sea until he was nearly fifty. Then, according to his own account in another letter, he made four voyages to South America. But historians can verify only two, possibly three, of them. He is named as a pilot under the Spaniard Ojeda, who in 1499 explored the coast east and south of

Columbus's landfall at Trinidad; and although not listed, Vespucci is assumed to have sailed as a geographer under Nuno Manoel in 1501, in a Portuguese expedition sent to explore the lower part of Brazil just discovered by Cabral. From 1508 to 1512 Vespucci held the position of Chief Pilot of Spain.

The voyage of 1501 is described in the selection below, from the *Mundus Novus* letter, published in 1503 or 1504.

Amerigo Vespucci to Lorenzo Piero di Medici, salutation.

In past days I wrote very fully to you of my return from the new countries, which have been found and explored with the ships, at the cost, and by the command, of this Most Serene King of Portugal [Manuel I]; and it is lawful to call it a new world, because none of these countries were known to our ancestors, and to all who hear about them they will be entirely new.

For the opinion of the ancients was that the greater part of the world beyond the equinoctial line [the equator] to the south was not land, but only sea, which they have called the Atlantic; and if they have affirmed that any continent is there, they have given many reasons for denying that it is inhabited. But this their opinion is false, and entirely opposed to the truth.

My last voyage has proved it, for I have found a continent in that southern part; [it is] more populous and more full of animals than our Europe, or

Asia, or Africa, and even more temperate and pleasant than any other region known to us. . . . I shall
write succinctly of the principal things only, and
the things most worthy of notice, and of being remembered, which I either saw or heard of in this new
world.

Vespucci describes how a fleet of three ships left Lisbon
May 14, 1501, "to discover new countries toward the
west." They sailed by way of Cape Verde (Africa) to
Brazil.

It was on the 7th of August, 1501, that we reached
those countries, thanking our Lord God with solemn
prayers, and celebrating a choral Mass. We knew that
land to be a continent, and not an island, from its
long beaches extending without trending round
[curving], the infinite number of inhabitants, the
numerous tribes and peoples, the numerous kinds of
wild animals unknown in our country, and many
others never seen before by us. . . .

We sailed along until we came to a point [Cape
St. Augustine] where the coast turned to the south.
The distance from the landfall to this point was
nearly three hundred leagues. . . . Where the said
point of land showed us the trend of the coast to the
south, we agreed to continue our voyage. . . . We
sailed along the coast for nearly five hundred leagues,
often going on shore and having intercourse with the
natives, who received us in a brotherly manner. . . .

Part of this continent is in the Torrid Zone, beyond the equinoctial line [the equator] toward the South Pole. But it begins at 8° beyond [south of] the equinoctial.

We sailed along the coast so far that we crossed the Tropic of Capricorn, and found ourselves where the Antarctic Pole was 50° above our horizon [Santa Cruz, near the Strait of Magellan]. . . . And I have known the nature of those people, their customs, the resources and fertility of the land, the [healthfulness] of the air, the positions of the celestial bodies in the heavens . . . over an eighth of the sphere, never seen by our ancestors.

Vespucci describes the "reddish" natives, their communal living, and the fertile country, abounding in strange fruits and herbs, and in pearls and gold.

This letter was translated from the Italian into the Latin language by Jocundus, interpreter, as everyone understands Latin who desires to learn about these voyages. . . . For, from the time the world began, so much has not been discovered touching the greatness of the earth and what is contained in it.

THE FOURTH PART: AMERICA

What Plato had imagined, Christopher Columbus had found. Daring the darkness of the Western Ocean, he had sailed to islands and a large transatlantic mainland.

Columbus wanted these lands to prove to be Cathay, but Amerigo Vespucci persuaded Europe that they were a new world. In 1507, one year after Columbus's death, a young German professor of geography, Martin Waldsee-müller, made the first world map showing the new lands as independent of the *orbis terrarum*. They appear as a barrier in the Ocean Sea, between western Europe and eastern Asia.

To go with his map Waldseemüller wrote an essay, in one section of which he explained that the new southern continent, since it was separate from Europe, Asia, and Africa, must be considered a "fourth part" of the world. (North America was not generally recognized to be a continent until the 1520's or later.)

He added that this "fourth part" might well be named after the man he thought was its discoverer: Americus Vesputius. It could be called "America."

Peter Martyr's brief notice of Columbus's discovery of South America in 1498 was not published until 1508. Meanwhile Waldseemüller had printed as an appendix to his essay Vespucci's letter about his four voyages, in which Vespucci falsely claimed to have reached South America in 1497.

By 1513 Waldseemüller had learned the truth; on his map of that year he gave Columbus credit for the discovery, even dropping the name "America." But by then Vespucci's high reputation in Italy and northern Europe, together with the neat parallelism of "America" to "Asia" and "Africa," had fixed the name in the public mind. It was extended to North America in 1538. (In Spain the new lands were officially called "The Indies" up until the latter half of the eighteenth century. *America*, the Latin form derived ultimately from German *Almerich*, means "rich in wheat.")

The following paragraphs from Waldseemüller's essay

Cosmographiae Introductio ("An Introduction to Cosmography") determined the name of the New World revealed by the epic voyage of Christopher Columbus.

In the sixth climate, toward the antarctic, are located both the recently discovered farthest part of Africa, and Zanzibar, the islands of Ceylon and lesser Java, and the fourth part of the world, which since Americus found it may be called Amerige (i.e., Americus's land) or America.

"America" won out over "Amerige" because of euphony. "Amerige" is a compound, the second part—*ge*—being the Greek word for "land."

Now, truly, as these regions have been more widely explored and another, fourth part has been found by Americus Vesputius, as may be learned from the following letters, I do not see why anyone may justly forbid that it be called Amerige—i.e., Americus's land, from the discoverer Americus, a man of keen mind; or America, since both Europe and Asia derived their names from women. Its situation and the customs of its people are clearly to be understood from the four voyages of Americus which follow.

Thus the earth is known to be divided into four parts. The first three parts are continents; the fourth is an island.

"Continents" were originally lands that were contiguous, touching each other; thus South America, which does not touch the only other continents then known (Europe, Asia, Africa), is called an "island."

Columbus's voyage of 1492 was a turning point in history. It brought about an enormous increase in man's knowledge of the earth, and changed his view of his own powers and limitations. Combined with the Portuguese conquests in the Indian Ocean, it caused new centers of commerce and Renaissance culture to spring up in the north and west of Europe—Lisbon, Seville, Antwerp, London—while the Italian cities declined.

These results did not appear immediately, however. In spite of Columbus's *Letter* (1493), Peter Martyr's *Decades* (1504), Vespucci's *Mundus Novus* letter (1503), and the *Paesi Novamente Retrovati* ("Countries Lately Found," 1507, a popular collection of narratives of discovery), the new lands were for some time veiled in mystery. Scholars and politicians needed more information about their resources. Mapmakers were baffled by conflicting theories of how the lands were related to the known continents of Europe, Asia, and Africa.

At the time of Columbus's death, in 1506, only the West Indies, the east coast of Central America, and the northern shoulder of South America could be drawn accurately on maps. "The Indies," the vestibule to the Americas, were shown near Cipangu. Newfoundland and New England, skirted by John Cabot (1497–98), were depicted as a part of northeastern Asia. The lines, sometimes broken off, tracing the Central and South American coasts, and the blank spaces behind these lines, left much to the imagination of Europe. (In his *Utopia*, 1516, Thomas More made some guesses about the interior of South America, placing deserts where there is really jungle.)

The maps of Bartholomew Columbus and Juan de la Cosa illustrate this incomplete knowledge. They show that the correct shape and location of the new lands had not yet been determined.

These maps were based on Columbus's four voyages to the New World, and on at least five others made around 1500. In 1493–96, Columbus had explored more of the West Indies (still looking for the Grand Khan), and had founded the colony of Isabella in Hispaniola—later moved by Bartholomew to Santo Domingo. In 1498, crossing the Atlantic farther south than before, Columbus struck the island of Trinidad and the coast of Venezuela, thus becoming the discoverer of South America. In 1502–04, he explored the Central American coast and encountered a canoe off Honduras laden with merchandise of the rich Aztec civilization to the northwest.

His successors, the "Little Discoverers" who sailed to the Indies after the Spanish Government canceled Columbus's monopoly of western exploration in 1495, included Ojeda (under whom Vespucci served), Vincente Yañez Pinzón (who discovered the upper part of Brazil and the Amazon), and Juan de la Cosa. These captains went to the pearl fisheries in the Gulf of Paria, Venezuela, found by Columbus on his third voyage, or sought a passage through the new lands to India—as Columbus did in 1502. In 1513 Ponce de León, looking for the Fountain of Youth, discovered Florida.

Attempts to colonize Central America and Venezuela failed, but during these years (1493–1509) the Spaniards established a modest empire in Hispaniola, Cuba, Puerto Rico, and Jamaica. Not much gold was found after all, but sugar cane, swine, and cattle were introduced, and proved profitable. When the Indians showed a lack of stamina for work in the fields and mines, the Spaniards took a fateful step: they introduced slavery in the New World by replacing the Indians with African captives.

In 1509 the second stage in the discovery of the New World began: the exploration and conquest of the interiors of Mexico, Central America, and South America. Just before this, in 1507, Vespucci's conviction that the new lands were separate from Asia had been reflected in Waldseemüller's world map. Waldseemüller showed the West Indies, a small, truncated North America, a slender Central America, and an extended South America (based on Vespucci's voyage of 1501–02 to southern Argentina). Even though Waldseemüller drew the "New World" (South America) as a large, isolated land in the midst of the Ocean Sea, he did not guess the size of the Americas.

Only after the feats of the conquistadores, the voyage of Magellan, and the entry of France into the race for colonies in the New World, would the truth emerge.

From 1509 to 1539 Balboa, Cortés, Pizarro, and Quesada, by almost superhuman efforts, conquered four mighty empires: Central America, Mexico, Peru, and New Granada (Colombia). When mapmakers took into account these realms, Magellan's voyage down the east coast of South America and part way up the west coast (1519–20), the coastal survey (North Carolina to Maine) made for the French king by Verrazano (1523–24), the exploration of the St. Lawrence by Cartier (1534–36, 1541–42), the wanderings of Cabeza de Vaca (1528–36), De Soto (1539–42) and Coronado (1540–41) through our South and Southwest, and the voyages of Cabrillo (1542) and Ferrelo (1543) along the California and Oregon coasts, they could finally show the New World in its full magnitude. The map of Ortelius (1587) reflects what was

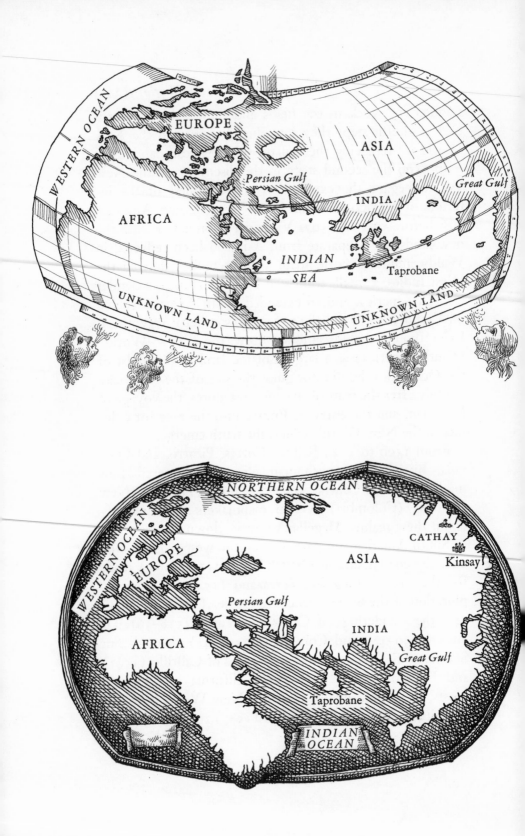

WESTERN OCEAN

EUROPE

ASIA

Persian Gulf

Great Gulf

INDIA

AFRICA

INDIAN
SEA

Taprobane

UNKNOWN LAND

UNKNOWN LAND

NORTHERN OCEAN

WESTERN OCEAN

EUROPE

ASIA

CATHAY

Kinsay

Persian Gulf

INDIA

AFRICA

Great Gulf

Taprobane

INDIAN
OCEAN

The map at left, copied from Ptolemy's Geography (around A.D. *150), shows the* orbis terrarum *or inhabited earth as fading off into unknown land on three sides. The Indian Ocean is enclosed, like a larger Mediterranean, and Asia is extended much too far in an east-west direction, covering 180° of longitude instead of the correct 126°. India is anvil-shaped instead of triangular, and Taprobane (Ceylon) is much too large. In spite of its inaccuracies, Ptolemy's map was the standard representation of the world through the Middle Ages. The chief change made by later cartographers was the substitution of the surrounding Ocean Sea for Ptolemy's fringe of "unknown land."*

Claudius Ptolemy was a famous mathematician, astronomer, and geographer who lived near Alexandria, Egypt. His Astronomy, *which depicted a stationary earth at the center of the universe, was called* Almagest *("The Greatest") by Arabs and men of the Middle Ages.*

Martellus's world map (about 1490) at left follows Ptolemy in its representation of Europe, India, and eastern Asia—except that Martellus has a surrounding Ocean Sea connected with the Indian Ocean. Marco Polo's thirteenth century voyage from Cathay (China) to the Persian Gulf and Bartholomew Dias's fifteenth century voyage from Portugal around the Cape of Good Hope had shown geographers that the Indian Ocean could be entered from both east and west. Martellus's long eastern Asiatic peninsula is a survival of Ptolemy's land bridge between China and the southern fringe of "unknown land" on Ptolemy's map. Columbus had the same conception of the world as Martellus. He and other early explorers at first identified America with Martellus's eastern Asiatic peninsula, and sought a passage through it to the "Great Gulf" and India. Columbus thought he was among islands just east of this peninsula when he landed in the West Indies.

Henricus Martellus Germanus was a German cartographer who drew his map in Florence, Italy, at the end of the fifteenth century.

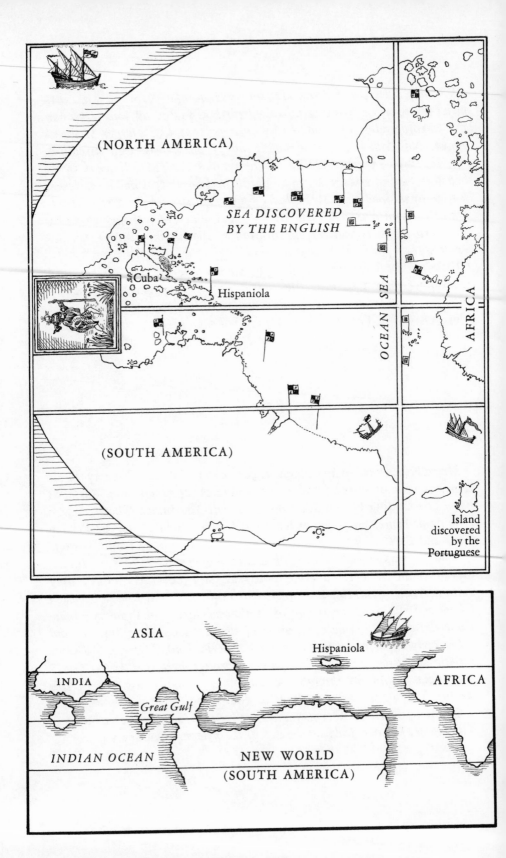

(NORTH AMERICA)

*SEA DISCOVERED
BY THE ENGLISH*

Cuba

Hispaniola

OCEAN SEA

AFRICA

(SOUTH AMERICA)

Island
discovered
by the
Portuguese

ASIA

Hispaniola

INDIA

AFRICA

Great Gulf

INDIAN OCEAN

NEW WORLD
(SOUTH AMERICA)

The world map of Juan de la Cosa (1500) is the oldest surviving map which shows the discoveries of Columbus, Cabot, and da Gama. The western section of the map shows, but does not give names to, North America and South America. Both areas, as well as the West Indies, are shown as a part of Asia. De la Cosa's drawing of Cuba as an island is said to have won him the enmity of Columbus, who insisted that it was a peninsula of the Asian mainland. There are English flags and a legend, "Sea discovered by the English," in the North American part of the map. The "Island discovered by the Portuguese" is probably Brazil. The inset portrait of St. Christopher covers the area where the Spanish still hoped to discover a water passage to the Indies.

Juan de la Cosa, an able seaman on the Niña on Columbus's first voyage, became a pilot on Columbus's second voyage, and later sailed to South America with Ojeda.

The map at left, a composite of three sketch maps by Bartholomew Columbus (1503–6), shows no advance over Juan de la Cosa's world map. That is, the new-found lands are still represented as a part of Asia. South America is drawn as a much enlarged eastern Asiatic peninsula connected by an isthmus. Presumably, this map reflects Christopher Columbus's theories about the location of the new lands.

Bartholomew Columbus made his three sketch-maps on the margin of a letter by Christopher Columbus to the Sovereigns Ferdinand and Isabella.

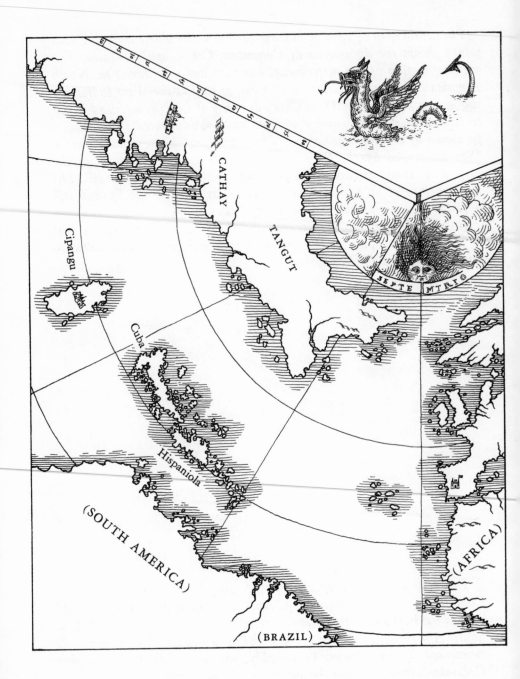

CATHAY

TANGUT

Cipangu

Cuba

Hispaniola

(SOUTH AMERICA)

(BRAZIL)

(AFRICA)

SEPTE MTRIO

Contarini's world map (1506) is the earliest printed map to show the new discoveries in the West. It is also the first to detach some of the new-found lands from Asia. In the section reproduced here, North America (labeled "Tangut" after a Chinese province described by Marco Polo) is still shown as a northeastern promontory of Asia, but is separated by a wide sea passage from the West Indies and South America, which are independent of Asia. Cipangu (Japan) is incorrectly placed only about 20°, and Cathay (China) only about 60°, west of the West Indies. South America appears as a vast detached southern continent. The water between South America and Asia reflects an early guess at the existence of the Pacific Ocean, perhaps from reports by the Portuguese in the Far East.

Giovanni Matteo Contarini was an Italian cartographer of the early sixteenth century.

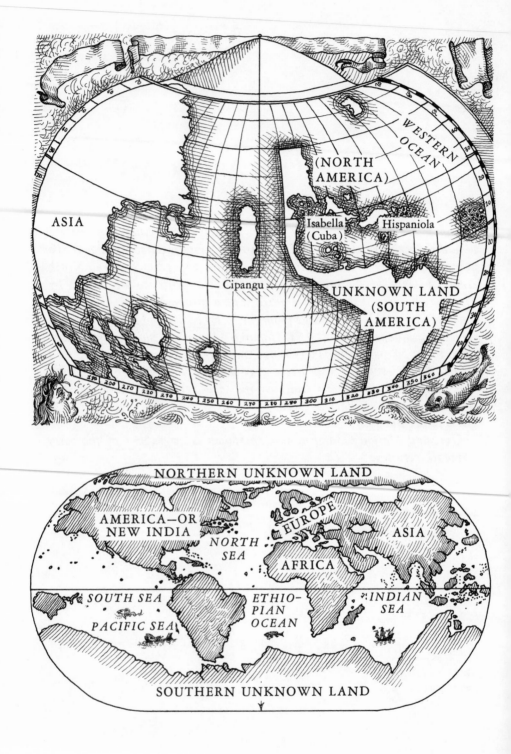

Waldseemüller's famous world map (1507) at left was the first to show the new lands as a "fourth part," completely separate from Europe, Asia, and Africa. South America is given something approaching its correct shape; the West Indies are laid down; North America is only a truncated peninsula but at least far removed from Asia. Cipangu (Japan) has strayed too far east and the Pacific Ocean is unnamed and too small, but in approximately the right position (mapmakers were soon calling it the "Eastern Ocean"). Waldseemüller's map became a best-seller and brought about general acceptance of Vespucci's startling theory that the Americas were a "new world."

Martin Waldseemüller was a young German professor of geography at the University of St. Dié in Lorraine. His work marks a transition from the traditional Ptolemaic geography toward modern scientific geography.

The world map of Ortelius (1587) at left, called "the Atlas of the Renaissance par excellence," completes the transition from Ptolemaic to modern geography. It is based not on the writings of the ancients but on firsthand information, and, except for the hypothetical Arctic and Antarctic continents, depicts the world approximately as we know it. By this time the chief features of the globe—outside the polar regions and the extreme north and south Pacific—were known.

Abraham Ortelius, born in Antwerp of German parents, is, along with his friend the famous Mercator, one of the first representatives of the new spirit of free inquiry in geography. (A Latin sentence at the bottom of the original map asks: "What can seem important in human affairs to one who knows eternity and the magnitude of the entire world?")

known of the Americas from the middle of the sixteenth
century on.

Thus, slowly, like secret writing appearing on a parchment held up to the fire, the outlines of two great continents were revealed.

The discovery of the Americas had a profound effect
upon the politics and economics of Europe. In 1493 Pope
Alexander VI issued his famous Bull, dividing the Atlantic
into two "spheres of influence." All lands found one
thousand miles or more west of the Cape Verde Islands
would belong to Spain; all new lands to the east of this
meridian or "line of demarcation" would be Portugal's. In
1494, by the Treaty of Tordesillas, aggressive King John II
of Portugal obtained a revision of this arrangement,
having the line drawn fifteen hundred miles west of the
Cape Verde Islands. As a result of this revision, Brazil became a Portuguese possession.

"I should like to have produced the will of Adam, con-
stituting [Spain and Portugal] his universal heirs," dryly
commented Francis I as he prepared to claim North
America for France.

Francis I wished to obtain a foothold in the New World
because he had heard reports of the gold and silver seized
by Cortés in Mexico. After Pizarro plundered Peru and
the Spaniards discovered the fabulously rich silver mines
of Potosi, Bolivia, in 1545, the New World stood forth
as a storehouse of gold and silver. Spanish plate fleets carried the precious metals to Europe, adding to the stock
of money in the Old World for the first time since the
fall of Rome. The French and English began to attack
these fleets and to hunt treasure for themselves in North
America.

Ironically the Spanish government was overwhelmed by its newly acquired wealth. The flood of bullion caused a drastic inflation in prices. Instead of investing the gold and silver to increase production in agriculture and industry, the government tried to hoard the metals, and actually went bankrupt three times before the end of the century, because of high prices. Northern Europe, where the new money *was* invested in trade and manufactures, profited most—especially Holland.

Nevertheless, an impressive overseas empire was won by Spain during the sixteenth century, an empire anticipated by Columbus in his *Journal* entries. By 1600 there were 160,000 Spaniards in the New World. Five million Indians were living increasingly as civilized men, under an elaborate colonial administration based on Spanish law. Churches, schools, monasteries, and universities were flourishing, from Mexico City to Lima. Even the mistreatment of the Indians, thanks to the impassioned protests of Las Casas, was less frequent. It was strictly against Spanish law to enslave the Indians. In the end, instead of being exterminated as happened in North America, they became an essential part of the South American civilization.

For Europe as a whole, the discovery of the Americas led not only to a startling increase in the supply of gold and silver, but to a new spirit of inquiry and optimism. The demonstration that revered authorities in geography had been mistaken provoked a skeptical attitude toward authorities in other fields, and a new emphasis on experiment. If Ptolemy could be wrong about the *orbis terrarum*, perhaps he was wrong about the motion of the planets—perhaps Copernicus was right.

The "second chance" offered to adventurers and persecuted minorities in the sparsely settled lands to the west changed the mood of Europe from the pessimism that had prevailed before 1492 to one of confidence and hope in the future.

Montaigne in his *Essays* and Shakespeare in *The Tempest* speculated about the "noble savage" described by explorers. Bacon planned a voyage of intellectual discovery in which he took "all knowledge" as his destination. Europeans no longer felt imprisoned in their narrow peninsula or doomed by the threat of the Moslem Turks advancing from the east. The finding of "another world" more than counterbalanced the loss of Constantinople (1453), the last relic of the Roman Empire which represented the order and security of the past.

Man was free, at last, to attempt to create the earthly paradise of which he had dreamed since the days of Plato.

And all this began with the achievement of one man, a Genoan with a limited education but with unlimited courage and persistence. Christopher Columbus had imagination, a supreme talent for navigation, and an instinct for discovery. Guided by little more than his compass and a strong religious faith, he sought Cathay. He found, instead, a new world, a hemisphere of islands and mainlands which more than doubled the area of Christian civilization and shifted the center of man's hopes, following in the wake of the *Santa María*, west across the Ocean Sea.

Bibliography

SOURCES FOR COLUMBUS'S VOYAGE OF 1492–3

Columbus, Christopher, *Journal,* tr. Cecil Jane. New York, Clarkson N. Potter, 1960.

Columbus, Christopher, *Journals and Other Documents on the Life and Voyages of Christopher Columbus,* tr. and ed. Samuel Eliot Morison. New York, The Heritage Press, 1963.

Columbus, Christopher, *Raccolta di Documenti e Studi,* 15 vols. Rome, Ministero della Pubblica Istruzione, 1892–1894.

Columbus, Christopher, *Select Documents,* tr. and ed. Cecil Jane, 2 vols. London, Hakluyt Society, 1930, 1933.

Columbus, Ferdinand, *The Life of the Admiral Christopher Columbus,* tr. Benjamin Keen. Rutgers University Press, 1959.

Las Casas, Bartolomé, *Historia de las Indias,* ed. A. M. Carlo and L. Hanke, 3 vols. Mexico City, Fondo de Cultura Económica, 1951.

Martyr, Peter, *De Orbe Novo,* tr. and ed. F. A. MacNutt, 2 vols. New York, G. P. Putnam's Sons, 1912.

Navarrete, D. Martin Fernández, *Colección de los Viages y Descubrimientos,* Vols. I and II. Madrid, La Imprenta Nacional, 1837.

Oviedo, Gonzalo Fernández de, *Historia General y Natural de las Indias,* ed. J. Bueso, Vol. I. Madrid, Biblioteca de Autores Españoles, 1959.

SOURCES FOR VOYAGES OF THE VIKINGS AND VESPUCCI

Haugen, Einar, tr. and ed. *Voyages to Vinland.* New York, Alfred A. Knopf, 1942.

Vespucci, Amerigo, *Letters,* tr. and ed. Clements R. Markham. London, Hakluyt Society, 1894.

LATER BOOKS ABOUT COLUMBUS AND THE AGE OF DISCOVERY

Ashe, Geoffrey, *Land to the West: St. Brendan's Voyage to America.* New York, The Viking Press, 1962.

Beazley, C. Raymond, *The Dawn of Modern Geography,* 3 vols. New York, Peter Smith, 1949 (First printed 1897).

Hart, Henry H., *Sea Road to the Indies.* New York, The Macmillan Company, 1950.

Herrmann, Paul, *The Great Age of Discovery.* New York, Harper & Brothers, 1958.

Kimble, George H. T., *Geography in the Middle Ages.* London, Methuen & Co. Ltd., 1938.

Levillier, Roberto, *América la Bien Llamada.* Buenos Aires, Editorial G. Kraft, 1948.

Madariaga, Salvador de, *Christopher Columbus.* New York, The Macmillan Company, 1940.

Morison, Samuel Eliot, *Admiral of the Ocean Sea: A Life of Christopher Columbus.* Boston, Little, Brown and Company, 1942.

Morison, Samuel Eliot, *Portuguese Voyagers to America in the Fifteenth Century.* Cambridge, Harvard University Press, 1940.

Morison, Samuel E. and Mauricio Obregón, *The Caribbean as Columbus Saw It.* Boston, Little, Brown and Company, 1964.

Nunn, George E., *The Geographical Conceptions of Columbus.* New York, American Geographical Society, 1924.

O'Gorman, Edmundo, *The Invention of America.* Bloomington, Indiana University Press, 1961.

Penrose, Boies, *Travel and Discovery in the Renaissance 1420–1620.* Cambridge, Harvard University Press, 1952.

Pohl, Frederick J., *Amerigo Vespucci: Pilot Major.* New York, Columbia University Press, 1944.

Skelton, R. A., Thomas E. Marston, and George D. Painter, *The Vinland Map and the Tartar Relation.* New Haven, Yale University Press, 1965.

Vignaud, Henri. *Histoire Critique de la Grande Enterprise de Christophe Colomb,* 2 vols. Paris, H. Welter, 1911.

A Timetable of Events

986 Bjarni Herjulfson, seeking Greenland, is blown off his course and sights North America.

1000 Leif Ericson, returning to Greenland from Norway, is also driven by a storm to North America and lands there.

1002 Leif Ericson explores the coasts of Labrador, Nova Scotia, and New England; he finds wild grapes, so names the country Vinland.

1004–6 Thorvald Ericson, Leif's brother, seeks valuable products in Vinland but is slain by Indians.

1271–95 Marco Polo crosses Asia to Peking, serves at the court of the Grand Khan for seventeen years, then returns to Venice.

September or October, 1451 Christopher Columbus, oldest child of the wool-weaver Domenico and his wife Susanna, is born in Genoa.

August, 1476 Columbus is wounded in a naval battle off Portugal, swims ashore, and eventually makes his way to Lisbon.

February, 1477   Columbus voyages in a Portuguese ship to Iceland.

1479   Columbus marries Dona Felipa Perestrello e Moniz in Lisbon; their son Diego is born the following year.

1482–83 or 1483–84   Columbus voyages in a Portuguese ship to the Gold Coast of Guinea, in Africa.

1485   A committee of experts under King John II of Portugal rejects Columbus's plan to reach the East by sailing west; Columbus goes to Spain to seek support for his "Enterprise" from Ferdinand and Isabella.

January, 1492   Queen Isabella, urged by Luís de Santangel, agrees to back Columbus's "Enterprise of the Indies."

April 17 and 30, 1492   Columbus is given Articles of Agreement, Title, Letter of Credence, Passport, and other documents by the Spanish Crown.

August 3, 1492   Columbus sails from Palos in the *Santa María*, accompanied by the *Niña* and *Pinta*, to find the western route to the Indies.

August 9 to September 6, 1492   Columbus makes repairs on his ships in the Canary Islands; he hears that a Portuguese fleet will intercept him, but sees no Portuguese vessels.

September 25, 1492   Martín Pinzón in the *Pinta* thinks he sights the imaginary island of Antillia, but it proves to be only a cloud.

October 10, 1492 The crew of the *Santa María* mutiny and demand that Columbus turn back; he persuades them to sail west for three more days.

October 12, 1492 The *Santa María*, *Niña*, and *Pinta* reach the island of Guanahaní, in the West Indies; Columbus takes possession for Ferdinand and Isabella and renames the island "San Salvador."

October 28, 1492 Columbus arrives at northeastern Cuba and believes it to be either Cipangu (Japan) or Cathay (China).

November 22, 1492 Martín Pinzón in the *Pinta* deserts the fleet to look for gold on "Babeque" (probably Great Inagua Island).

December 6, 1492 The *Santa María* and *Niña* reach western Hispaniola at a harbor Columbus names Puerto de San Nicolas (Port St. Nicholas).

December 24, 1492 The *Santa María* is wrecked on a reef off the north coast of Hispaniola, near Cape Haitien.

December 26, 1492 to January 2, 1493 Columbus founds the colony of La Navidad on Caracol Bay, opposite the site of the wreck; he leaves thirty-nine colonists here.

January 6, 1493 The *Pinta*, under Martín Pinzón, rejoins the *Niña;* Pinzón has found much gold in central Hispaniola.

January 13, 1493   Columbus's men clash with armed Indians at Samaná Bay, in eastern Hispaniola.

January 16, 1493   Columbus, with the *Niña* and *Pinta*, leaves the West Indies for Spain.

February 12–15, 1493   A great storm batters the *Niña* and *Pinta*—the two ships are separated.

February 17–24, 1493   Columbus in the *Niña* anchors off the Azores, where half his men are imprisoned by the hostile Portuguese ruler; he recovers his men and departs.

February 26 to March 3, 1493   A second storm nearly sinks the *Niña;* in the evening of March 3, the lookout sights the coast of Portugal.

March 4, 1493   Columbus sails into Lisbon Harbor; the next day he is questioned by Bartholomew Dias.

March 9, 1493   Columbus is received outside Lisbon by King John II, who tries to conceal his jealousy of Columbus's success.

March 15, 1493   Columbus in the *Niña* returns to Palos, completing his conquest of the Western Ocean; the *Pinta* arrives later in the day.

1493   Pope Alexander VI issues a bull granting Spain a monopoly

of new lands discovered 1,000 miles or more west of the Cape
Verde Islands.

1493–96 Columbus makes his second voyage to the New World;
he again seeks the Grand Khan, and founds the colony of
Isabella in Hispaniola, but suffers many setbacks.

1498–1500 Columbus makes his third voyage to the New World;
he discovers South America, and finds rich pearl fisheries off
the coast of Venezuela.

1501–2 Amerigo Vespucci sails on a Portuguese expedition to
Brazil and Argentina.

1503 Amerigo Vespucci, in a letter to Piero Francesco di Medici,
declares that South America is a new world, separate from
Europe, Asia, and Africa.

1502–4 Columbus makes his fourth voyage to the New World;
he explores the east coast of Central America, looking for a
strait to the Indian Ocean.

May 20, 1506 Christopher Columbus dies in Valladolid, Spain.

1507 Martin Waldseemüller makes the first world map showing
the new lands as independent of Europe, Asia, and Africa;
he suggests that the southern continent be named "America"
after Amerigo Vespucci, who explored its eastern coast.

Cast of Characters

Pope Alexander VI. Worldly pope, a Spaniard who partly owes his election to support of Ferdinand and Isabella. In return, by Bull of 1493, grants them a monopoly of new lands discovered west of a certain meridian in the Atlantic.

Aristotle. Famous Greek philosopher, the "intellect" of Plato's school and tutor of Alexander the Great. His theory of a narrow ocean between Europe and Asia appeals to Columbus.

Martin Behaim. Rather conceited German cosmographer whom Columbus may have known in Lisbon. Claims to have sailed on important Portuguese voyages, later returns to Nuremberg and makes a famous globe on which Asia is extended too far to the east.

St. Brendan. Sixth century Irish abbot who founds a monastery at Clonfert, voyages to Wales and Scottish isles. In legend, the hero of a seven-year Odyssey through the Atlantic to an earthly paradise, the Land of Promise.

Juan de Castañeda. Zealous temporary ruler of the Azores (Portuguese possessions) who imprisons half Columbus's crew as poachers. An angry young man who is outwitted by Columbus.

[265]

Bartholomew Columbus. Christopher's loyal brother, a skilled mapmaker. Seeks support for the "Enterprise of the Indies" in England and France.

Christopher Columbus. Chartmaker, navigator, business agent of Genoa. Imaginative, boastful, religious, brave. Supremely confident that he can reach the East by sailing west. Discoverer of the West Indies and South America.

Diego Columbus. Young son of Columbus and his wife Felipa. Accompanies his father to Palos, spends six years in the monastery at La Rabida. A future admiral of Spain.

Domenico Columbus. Columbus's good-hearted but shiftless father, who is too fond of a cup of wine. City of Santo Domingo, in Hispaniola, is named in his memory.

Ferdinand Columbus. Son of Columbus and Beatriz de Harana. Scholarly, devoted to his father, with whom he sails on fourth voyage to New World. Author of *The Life of the Admiral Christopher Columbus* (1571).

Bartholomew Dias. Heroic navigator, the first European to round the Cape of Good Hope. Interviews Columbus on Columbus's return from the West Indies.

Leif Ericson. Gallant Viking leader. A daring navigator who sails on a new course between Norway and Greenland and accidentally reaches North America.

Thorvald Ericson. Leif Ericson's brother who wishes to exploit the newfound Vinland, appreciates its beauty, but suffers a tragic fate there.

King Ferdinand. Wily politician, able diplomat. Rather cold, but contributes large funds to Columbus's expedition after being convinced by Isabella of its value. Wounded by an assassin in 1492.

The Grand Khan. Ruler of the Mongol Empire which extended over China in thirteenth and fourteenth centuries. Eagerly sought by Columbus in the West Indies (which Columbus considers to be Cathay) because of Marco Polo's descriptions of his wealth.

King Guacanagarí. Chivalrous cacique (native chief) of north-western Haiti. Generous to Columbus's men, a "noble savage" more Christian than the "Christians" who plan to enslave his people.

Bjarni Herjulfson. Alert Viking merchant, devoted to his father. Is said to have sighted Vinland (North America) fourteen years before Leif Ericson did.

Queen Isabella. Gracious, auburn-haired, blue-eyed queen. Conventionally pious, appreciates Columbus's crusading ideals. Prejudiced against the Jews, whom she drives out of Spain.

King John II. Able, aggressive Portuguese ruler who has sent his seamen beyond the Cape of Good Hope. Shows some interest in Columbus's westward voyage, but prefers the eastern route to India.

Juan de La Cosa (1). Master and part owner of the *Santa María* who abandons his ship when it is sinking, apparently out of spite toward Columbus.

Juan de La Cosa (2). Able seaman on the *Niña* who later becomes a pilot and accompanies Ojeda on voyage of exploration to South America. Makes early map showing the New World as part of Asia.

Bartolomé de Las Casas. The first priest ordained in the New World, later a bishop. A fiery champion of the Indians against their Spanish oppressors. Author of the *Historia de las Indias* (1527–63).

John Mandeville. English physician, exiled to Belgium because of a homicide he committed in his youth. Author of fictitious *Travels* (1360–62), a medieval best seller which influences later navigators.

Peter Martyr. Talented young Italian humanist who becomes the first historian of Columbus's voyages and invents the phrase "The New World" to describe lands found by Columbus.

Duke of Medina Celi. Wealthy Spanish nobleman who agrees to provide Columbus with "three or four well-equipped caravels" for his "Enterprise," but sends him first to Ferdinand and Isabella to obtain their consent.

Fray Juan Pérez. Head of the Franciscan monastery of La Rabida, near Palos. An enthusiast for Columbus's "Enterprise of the Indies" who sends Columbus to Seville to meet influential Spaniards.

Martín Pinzón. Veteran mariner, leading citizen of Palos. Bluff, strong-minded, suspicious of outsiders. Helps Columbus recruit crews, but later becomes jealous of him, disobeys orders.

Plato. Ancient Greek philosopher whose imaginary Atlantic island of Atlantis, and "boundless continent" beyond, draws mariners westward. An aristocrat, a champion wrestler in his youth.

Marco Polo. A businessman of Venice, keen observer, the greatest traveler of the Middle Ages. Journeys 30,000 miles through Asia, serves the Grand Khan, writes a popular *Book* about the marvels of the East which inspires Columbus and other navigators.

Luís de Santangel. Far-seeing Keeper of the Privy Purse under King Ferdinand who urges Isabella to show "a resolute spirit" and back Columbus. Offers to finance the expedition himself.

Luís de Torres. A *converso* (Spanish Jew converted to Christianity) taken on Columbus's expedition as an interpreter because of his knowledge of Hebrew and Arabic.

Paolo Toscanelli. Florentine physician, amateur geographer, who believes one can reach the East by sailing west and encourages Columbus in his "Enterprise."

Amerigo Vespucci. Shrewd merchant-explorer of Florence who voyages to southern Argentina, writes entertaining account of his explorations, is first to say clearly that new lands are not part of Asia, but a New World.

Martin Waldseemüller. Young German professor of geography who believes Amerigo Vespucci's claim to have discovered South America and hence names that continent "America." Makes first world map showing New World as a "fourth part," separate from Europe, Asia, and Africa.

Index

Acul Bay, 184, 185

Adam of Bremen, *History*, 57–58

Africa, voyages to, 11, 16–17, 22, 220, 260

Alexander VI, Pope, 252, 262–63

Alfragan, 19, 92

Amazons, 46, 48–49

America, name for New World, 238–39

Antillia (Island of the Seven Cities), 6, 43–46, 94, 95, 97, 99, 122, 152, 261

Arawak Indians, *see* Ciguayo Indians, Taino Indians

Argentina, 243, 263

Aristotle, 18, 53, 92, 144

Astrolabe, 12, 52, 207

Atlantic Ocean, 4–6, 7–13; pre-Columbian legends of, 2, 4–5, 29–53; early voyages in, 6, 9–12, 15–16; Norse voyages, 7, 9–10, 57–77; *see also* Voyages

Atlantis, 5, 7; descriptions of, 29–33, 36

Azores, 11, 12, 18, 19, 43, 97, 98, 99, 213–14, 215–18, 262

Babeque, 175, 176, 177, 179–80, 181, 202, 261

Bahamas, Columbus in, 138–63

Bariay Bay, 161

Barinthus, *Navigatio*, 37, 39–43

Behaim, Martin, globe of, 44–45, 112, 157

Brazil, 235, 236–37, 242, 244, 263

Brendan, Saint, voyages of, 6, 36, 37–43

Cabot, John, 240

Cadamosto, Alvisa da, 12

Canary Islands, 2, 8–9, 10, 11, 37, 92, 185; Columbus in, 112–16, 260

Cape Haitien, 186, 191, 192, 261

Cape of Good Hope, 22

Cape St. Vincent, 11, 15, 98, 180, 218, 219, 222, 223

Cape Verde Islands, 12, 252, 263

Caracol Bay, 186, 188, 191, 261

Caravels, 11, 12, 182; supplied to Columbus by town of Palos, 99, 100, 103

Carib Indians, 179–80, 183, 199–200, 202, 203

Castañeda, Juan de, 214, 215–18

Cathay, *see* China

Central America, 240, 242, 243

Charts, 16, 94, 95, 122, 125, 158

China (Cathay), 13, 16, 46, 83, 92, 97; Marco Polo's description of, 85, 87–88; Columbus' search for, 149, 158, 237

Christianity: Columbus' aim to spread, 21, 24, 83, 96, 170, 172, 173–74

Cibao, 188, 196, 201

Ciguayo Indians, 202, 203–5, 262

Cipangu, *see* Japan

Columbus, Bartholomew (brother), 14, 16, 20, 22, 23; world map of, 242, 246 (illus.)

Columbus, Christopher, 259; boyhood, 13–14; voyages as workman and seaman, 14–16, 16–17, 259, 260; at Lisbon, 15–20, 220–22; chartmaking business with brother, 16, 17, 20; in Spain, 20–24; appearance and character of, 81–84; third voyage of, 231–33, 242, 263; death, 240, 263; second voyage of, 242, 263; fourth voyage of, 242, 263

[271]